WASTEWATER TREATMENT PLANT OPERATIONS MADE EASY

Wastewater Treatment Plant Operations Made Easy

A Practical Guide for Licensure

FRANK R. SPELLMAN
JOANNE DRINAN

DEStech Publications

Wastewater Treatment Plant Operations Made Easy

DEStech Publications, Inc.
439 North Duke Street
Lancaster, Pennsylvania 17602 U.S.A.

Printed in the United States of America
10   9   8   7   6   5   4   3

Main entry under title:
  Wastewater Treatment Plant Operations Made Easy

A DEStech Publications book
Bibliography: p.
Includes index p. 229

ISBN No. 978-1-932078-09-1

Table of Contents

Preface

WASTEWATER Treatment Plant Operations Made Easy: A Practical Guide for Licensure is more than just a readily accessible source of information for review in preparing wastewater personnel for operator certification and/or licensure, it is a resource manual. It contains wastewater treatment information, data, operational material, process control procedures and problem solving, safety and health information, new trends in wastewater treatment administration/technology, and numerous sample problem-solving practice sets. In short, the text's most important feature is its multifaceted presentation. For example,

- It is designed as a guide to hands-on, day-to-day plant operations.
- It covers the basic "nuts and bolts" technical aspects of plant operations required of wastewater operators.
- It gives today's wastewater operators information they need to expand their knowledge—which will aid them in the efficient operation of a wastewater treatment plant.
- It provides the user with the basic information and sample problem-solving sets needed to prepare for state licensing/certification examinations.
- It provides user-friendly, straightforward, plain-English reference material—a handbook of information not only for operators but also for the plant manager, plant superintendent, chief operator, lab technician, maintenance operator, and utility manager.
- When used as part of a formal training program, the present text provides a structured training activity, which may be used by plant trainers to meet Continuing Professional Education (CPE) requirements.

✓ *Note:* For CPE credit, it is important to check with State agencies to ensure material meets applicable standards. Each State has its own requirements.

The text's primary goal is to enhance the understanding, awareness and abilities of practicing operators and those who aspire to be operators.

Written in a straightforward style, this book details all the major unit processes in a wastewater plant and the practical aspects of achieving permit compliance. It then reviews technical materials covered on certification and licensure exams. One message conveyed by the text is that none of us are chained to the knowledge we already have—we should strive to increase our technical knowledge and expertise constantly. For those preparing for operator's licensing, this is critical; wastewater treatment is a complex, but learnable, discipline. For seasoned, licensed veteran operators, continuous review is also critical, because wastewater treatment is an evolving, dynamic field.

Contrary to long-held belief, treating wastewater is not just an art but instead is both an art and a science. Treating wastewater successfully requires a broad range of experience as well as technical expertise. This is where the "Made Easy" format comes in. From collecting and pumping influent, treating the waste stream through managing biosolids, this text provides easy to understand state-of-the-art information. Moreover, it is, in essence, a handheld reference text—one that enables the practitioner of the artful-science of wastewater treatment to qualify for certification, re-certification and/or to refresh his or her memory in a precise, efficient, and effective manner.

The text was prepared to help operators obtain licensure and to operate wastewater treatment plants properly. Can it be used as a textbook in technical training courses or in technical schools and community colleges? Absolutely. In fact, it is highly recommended for instruction wherever practical information about wastewater must be clearly conveyed.

Note that the text does not discuss the specific content of any licensure examination. It reviews the wastewater operator's job-related knowledge identified by the examination developers as essential for a minimally competent Class VI through Class I or Grade I through Grade V wastewater treatment plant operator. Every attempt has been made to make the text as comprehensive as possible while maintaining its compact, practical format.

The bottom line: The text is not designed simply for "teaching to" operator licensure exams, although it is immediately apparent to users that the material presented will help them pass the licensure exams. Moreover, all the material in the text has been selected for practical use and application. We present applied math, chemistry and lab operations by way of real world examples.

To assure correlation to modern practice and design, illustrative problems are structured in terms of commonly used treatment parameters and cover those unit processes typically found in current wastewater treatment systems.

The text is accessible to those with no experience in wastewater treatment operations.

Each chapter ends with a Self-Test to help evaluate your mastery of the concepts discussed. Before going on to the next chapter, take the Self-Test, compare your answers to the key, and review information for any problems missed. A comprehensive final exam can be found at the end of the text.

Will *Wastewater Treatment Plant Operations Made Easy* help you obtain a passing score on certification exams? Yes. If you follow it, use it, and reuse it, it will help.

✓ *Note:* The symbol ✓ (check mark) displayed in various sections throughout the text indicates a point is especially important and should be studied carefully.

CHAPTER 1

Introduction

"The construction of technological networks in American cities for the transmission of water, wastewater, power, communications, freight, and people dramatically altered the context of city life and the effect that urban centers had upon their surrounding environments."[1]

1.1 SETTING THE STAGE

WASTEWATER treatment has been called the "last line of defense" against water pollution, and less portentously has been defined as the cleaning of used water and sewage so it can be returned safely to our environment. Wastewater treatment plant operations are a vital part of a nation's effort to protect water resources. Clean water in many senses is the goal of wastewater treatment.

Except in nature—through the self-purification process that occurs in streams—wastewater is not normally cleaned without human intervention. This intervention is important for two reasons:

(1) We need to treat wastewater to protect the public from disease-causing bacteria and viruses (conventional wastewater treatment accomplishes this by disinfecting the wastewater).
(2) We need to treat wastewater to protect water quality.

1.2 WASTEWATER TREATMENT: THE PROCESS

There are three main sources of wastewater: (1) homes, (2) industries, and (3) storm runoff and groundwater. *Domestic* wastewater includes human and

---

[1]Tarr, J., *The Search for the Ultimate Sink: Urban Pollution in Historical Perspective.* Akron, Ohio: University of Akron Press, p. xxx, 1996.

1

household wastes from toilets, sinks, baths and showers. *Industrial* wastewater includes chemicals and other wastes from factories, food service operations, schools, businesses, airports, shopping centers, etc. *Storm runoff* and *Groundwater* consists of the water that collects in street drains during a storm, as well as groundwater that seeps through cracks in sewer and interceptor lines.

✓ *Note:* On average, each person in the U.S. contributes 50–100 gallons of wastewater every day.

Wastewater treatment plants clean the waste stream by removing solids, reducing organic matter and pollutants, and by restoring oxygen.

Wastewater treatment usually includes two main steps: primary and secondary treatment. Wastewater treatment also includes the processing of two waste products: contaminated water and waste solids (sludge or biosolids). In *primary treatment*, sanitary or separate sewers carry wastewater from homes and businesses to the treatment plant. In some areas, "combined" sewers carry storm runoff, as well. The wastewater *influent* is conveyed via interceptor lines and pumping stations (lift stations) to the plant. It first enters the plant through *bar screens,* which block passage of trash (such as rags or sticks). The trash is collected and properly disposed of, while the waste stream continues flowing to the *grit chamber.* Here the waste stream is slowed down, allowing sand, grit and other heavy solids to settle in the chamber from which they are removed. From the grit chamber the waste stream flows into a *primary clarifier* (sedimentation tank), which lets smaller particles settle. Scrapers or other devices collect the solid matter that remains (*primary sludge*) plus scum or grease floating on top of the tank. Primary treatment process removes 40–50% of the solids.

Secondary treatment refines the primary process, so that 85–90% of the contaminants are removed. After primary sedimentation, the waste stream flows into an *aeration basin.* Aeration basins supply large volumes of air to a mixture of wastewater, bacteria and other microorganisms. Oxygen in the air speeds the growth of microorganisms that consume harmful organic matter in the wastewater. The waste stream leaves the aeration basin and flows into a *secondary clarifier* (secondary sedimentation) where the microorganisms and solid wastes form clumps and settle. A portion of the mixture, called *activated sludge,* is usually mixed with air again and reused in the aeration basins. The waste stream is then *disinfected* (usually by using chlorine, UV, ozone, or some other disinfectant) before it leaves the treatment plant. The disinfectant kills disease-causing organisms in the water.

After treatment, the water is returned to a local stream or river, termed the *receiving body.* Typically, it is also used in land applications for agriculture and other purposes.

As mentioned, wastewater treatment includes the processing of two waste products: contaminated water and solids. During the treatment process described above, solids (i.e., sludge) are continuously being removed from the waste stream. Eventually, raw sludge is treated separately from the liquid waste. For example, raw sludge may be treated (thickened) to remove some of its water (which is returned to the headworks for re-treatment), and then further processed to produce biosolids. This additional processing may include sludge stabilization, dewatering, and utilization.

✓ *Note:* Wastewater solids have traditionally been grouped under the names sewage sludge or sludge—labels widely recognized throughout the wastewater industry and used by regulators. The term sewage sludge, however, conjures up connotations that do not fit the value of this waste product. Such a valuable reuse product should have a name that more readily fits its real worth. Vesilind makes this point best in the following:

"Sludge, in my opinion, should be thought of as a waste product with value (no contradiction) and a material which should find its proper use, not just a method of disposal . . . to some people, sludge is still an ugly four-letter word. To others (and to me) it is a residual of our society which must be treated and used to the maximum benefit of mankind, recognizing that mankind is but one species on this wonderful planet."[2]

Keeping Vesilind's point in mind, some have rechristened wastewater sludge as *biosolids*. For a fitting definition of the term biosolids, we need only turn to the Water Environment Federation's (WEF's) 1995 definition: *Biosolids* is defined as a "primary organic, solid municipal wastewater treatment product that can be beneficially used."[3]

Thus, sludge—that ugly "four-letter" word—has been properly renamed, biosolids—a term or name that is more fitting and reflective of its true value. And since biosolids has value as a product that can be beneficially reused, it certainly should not be classified as a waste product.

There are wastewater practitioners in the real world who will take issue with the authors' sentiments on this name issue; that is, biosolids is a legitimate term for sludge. Moreover, there are those who might argue that in this instance common sense has been taken to the extreme. (Was it not Voltaire who stated: "Common sense is not that common."?) The point is that in this text we use the term biosolids in place of the old term sludge—whenever it is feasible.[4]

In *sludge stabilization,* raw sludge is allowed to decompose in a *digester.* In some cases, assorted chemicals are used for stabilization. Stabilized biosolids

---

[2]Vesilind, P. A., *Treatment and Disposal of Wastewater Sludges.* Ann Arbor, MI: Ann Arbor Publishers, Inc., pp. 315–316, 1980.

[3]WEF. *Biosolids Composting.* Alexandria, VA: Water Environment Federation, p. 179, 1995.

[4]Spellman, F. R., *Dewatering Biosolids.* Lancaster, PA: Technomic Publishing Company, p. 3, 1997.

have no odor and are free of disease-causing organisms. In the *dewatering* process, as the name suggests, most of the water from the mixture is removed. Filters, drying beds, and various kinds of filter presses are used. *Sludge utilization* involves the application of biosolids (in cake or harmless humus form) to be disposed of by land application, composting, incineration, or landfilling.

1.3 WASTEWATER TREATMENT: THE MODEL

Figure 1.1 shows a basic schematic of a conventional wastewater treatment process: primary and secondary treatment using the activated sludge process. We use this as the model, the prototype of wastewater treatment processes throughout this text. It should be pointed out, however, that in secondary treatment [which provides biochemical oxygen demand (BOD) removal beyond what is achievable by simple sedimentation] two alternate approaches (besides activated sludge) are also commonly used (i.e., trickling filters and oxidation ponds). Accordingly, though our focus is on the activated sludge process, we also cover the operation of these other two important and commonly used processes.

A note about Figure 1.1. We use Figure 1.1 in the form shown here; we also use subsequent renditions of it as we progress, chapter by chapter, through the presentation and discussion of each unit process. For example, as we begin our discussion of each unit process, step-by-step, we use Figure 1.1, but only label the sections already discussed and the section being discussed. In essence, we start with a blank diagram and fill in the unit processes as we progress. Thus, as we proceed we gradually fill in and "build" the schematic shown in Figure 1.1. Based on our experience, this sequential construction of the entire conventional wastewater treatment process aids the reader in understanding how all the various unit processes follow and tie into each other. Again, even though the model shown in Figure 1.1 does not include all unit processes currently used in wastewater treatment, we do not ignore the other major processes. Trickling filters, rotating biological contactors (RBCs), oxidation ponds, and incineration and land application of biosolids are all presented and discussed.

1.4 WASTEWATER TREATMENT: TERMINOLOGY AND DEFINITIONS

In addition to enlightening us about common sense, Voltaire also stated: "If you wish to converse with me, please define your terms." This certainly makes sense when we consider that every branch of science and technology has its own terms with their own definitions. Likewise, this is the case in wastewater treatment. For example, terms such as activated sludge, clarifier, anoxic, biochemical oxygen demand (BOD), daily discharge, facultative, food, micro-

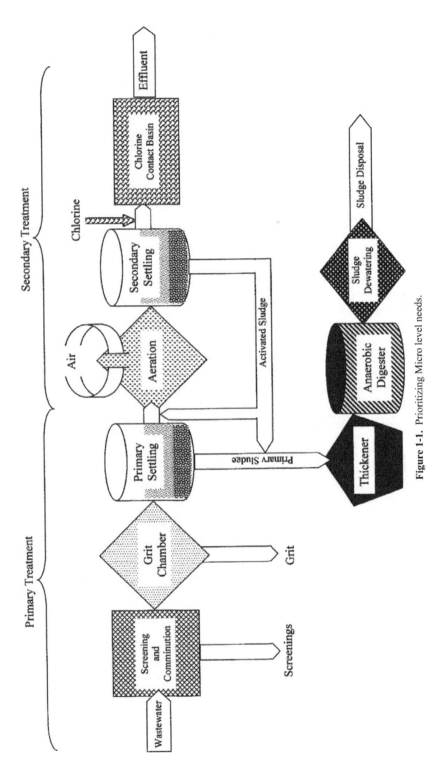

Figure 1-1. Prioritizing Micro level needs.

5

organism ratio, grit, mixed liquor, dewatering, conditioning, stabilization, and others are typically associated with (and some are unique to) the wastewater profession; others combine words from many different professions. Wastewater treatment borrows ideas and words from engineering, biology, mathematics, hydrology, water hydraulics, physics, chemistry, and other disciplines.

In this introductory chapter, we identify and define many of the terms unique to wastewater treatment and other related terms. Those terms not listed or defined in the following section will be defined at the end of each chapter (in the "key terms" section) or as they appear in the text.

Why do we not include these terms and their definitions in a glossary at the end of the text (the common practice in most technical publications)? Based on our experience, it is important to start out a learning activity on the right foot, using the correct terms and, more importantly, providing understanding early in the presentation for those terms that follow in subsequent chapters. Also, terms presented at the outset are more likely to be consulted and remembered.

1.4.1 TERMINOLOGY AND DEFINITIONS

✓ *Note:* In the Chapter Self-Test, you will be quizzed on many of these terms.

- *Activated sludge*—the solids formed when microorganisms are used to treat wastewater by means of the activated sludge treatment process. It includes organisms, accumulated food materials and waste products from the aerobic decomposition process.
- *Advanced waste treatment*—a treatment technology used to produce an extremely high-quality discharge.
- *Aerobic*—conditions in which free, elemental oxygen is present. Also used to describe organisms, biological activity, or treatment processes which require free oxygen.
- *Afterburner*—a device that includes an auxiliary fuel burner and combustion chamber to incinerate combustible gas contaminants.
- *Air emission*—for stationary sources, is the release or discharge of a pollutant by an owner or operator into the ambient air either by means of a stack or as a fugitive dust, mist, or vapor as the result of a manufacturing or forming process.
- *Air pollutant*—dust, fumes, smoke, and other particulate matter, vapor, gas, odorous substances, or any combination thereof.
- *Anaerobic*—conditions in which no oxygen (free or combined) is available. Also used to describe organisms, biological activity or treatment processes that function in the absence of oxygen.

- *Anoxic*—conditions in which no free, elemental oxygen is present; the only source of oxygen is combined oxygen such as that found in nitrate compounds. Also used to describe biological activity or treatment processes that function only in the presence of combined oxygen.
- *Autogenous/autothermic combustion*—incinerator burning of a wet organic material where the moisture content is at such a level that the heat of combustion of the organic material is sufficient to vaporize the water and maintain combustion. No auxiliary fuel is required except for start-up.
- *Average monthly discharge limitation*—the highest allowable discharge over a calendar month.
- *Average weekly discharge limitation*—the highest allowable discharge over a calendar week.
- *Biochemical oxygen demand, BOD_5*—the amount of organic matter that can be biologically oxidized under controlled conditions (5 days @ 20°C in the dark).
- *Biosolids*—(from Merriam-Webster's Collegiate Dictionary, Tenth Edition): biosolid *n*-solid organic matter recovered from a sewage treatment process and used especially as fertilizer—usually used in plural.

✓ *Note:* In this text (and all other Spellman/Drinan texts on wastewater topics), the term biosolids is used in many places (activated sludge being the exception) to replace the term sludge. As mentioned, the authors (along with others in the field) view the term sludge as inappropriate for denoting or describing biosolids.

- *Biosolids cake*—the solid discharged from a dewatering apparatus.
- *Buffer*—a substance or solution that resists changes in pH.
- *Burning rate*—the volume of solid waste incinerated or the amount of heat released during incineration.
- *Cake solids discharge rate*—the dry solids cake discharge from a centrifuge, which is expressed as follows:

dry cake solids discharge rate = (dry solids feed rate) × (solids recovery)

- *Carbonaceous biochemical oxygen demand, CBOD*—the amount of biochemical oxygen demand that can be attributed to carbonaceous material.
- *Centrate*—the effluent or liquid portion of biosolids removed by or discharged from a centrifuge.

- *Chemical oxygen demand (COD)*—the amount of chemically oxidizable material present in wastewater.
- *Clarifier*—a device designed to permit solids to settle or rise and be separated from the flow. Also known as a settling tank or sedimentation basin.
- *Coliform*—a type of bacteria used to indicate possible human or animal contamination of water.
- *Combined sewer*—a collection system that carries both wastewater and stormwater flows.
- *Combustion air*—the air used for burning fuel.
- *Comminution*—a process to shred solids into smaller, less harmful particles.
- *Composite sample*—a combination of individual samples taken in proportion to flow.
- *Daily discharge*—the discharge of a pollutant measured during a calendar day or any 24-hour period that reasonably represents a calendar day for the purposes of sampling. Limitations expressed as weight are total mass (weight) discharged over the day. Limitations expressed in other units are average measurements of the day.
- *Daily maximum discharge*—the highest allowable values for a daily discharge.
- *Detention time*—the theoretical time water remains in a tank at a given flow rate.
- *Dewatering*—the removal or separation of a portion of water present in a sludge or slurry.
- *Discharge Monitoring Report (DMR)*—the monthly report required by the treatment plant's NPDES discharge permit.
- *Dissolved oxygen (DO)*—free or elemental oxygen that is dissolved in water.
- *Drying hearth*—a solid surface in an incinerator upon which wet waste materials or waste matter that may turn to liquid before burning are placed to dry or to burn with the help of hot combustion gases.
- *Effluent*—the flow leaving a tank, channel or treatment process.
- *Effluent limitation*—any restriction imposed by the regulatory agency on quantities, discharge rates, or concentrations of pollutants that are discharged from point sources into state waters.
- *Excess air*—the amount of air required beyond the theoretical air requirements for complete combustion.
- *Facultative*—organisms that can survive and function in the presence or absence of free, elemental oxygen.

- *Fecal coliform*—a type of bacteria found in the bodily discharges of warm-blooded animals. Used as an indicator organism.
- *Filtrate*—the effluent or liquid portion of biosolids removed by or discharged from a centrifuge.
- *Flashpoint*—the lowest temperature at which evaporation of a substance produces sufficient vapor to form an ignitable mixture with air, near the surface of the liquid.
- *Floc*—solids designed to form larger particles that will settle better.
- *Fluidized bed combustion*—oxidation of combustible material within a bed of solid, inert particles that act as a fluid under the action of vertical hot airflow.
- *Flume*—a flow rate measurement device.
- *Fly ash*—airborne combustion residue from burning fuel.
- *Food-to-microorganism ratio (F/M)*—an activated sludge process-control calculation based upon the amount of food (BOD_5 or COD) available per pound of mixed liquor volatile suspended solids.
- *Forced draft*—the positive pressure created by the action of a fan or blower that supplies the primary or secondary combustion air in an incinerator.
- *Furnace*—a combustion chamber, an enclosed structure in which heat is produced.
- *Grab sample*—an individual sample collected at a randomly selected time.
- *Grit*—heavy inorganic solids such as sand, gravel, egg shells, or metal filings.
- *Incineration*—an engineered process using controlled flame combustion to thermally degrade waste material.
- *Industrial wastewater*—wastes associated with industrial manufacturing processes.
- *Infiltration/inflow*—extraneous flows in sewers; defined by Metcalf & Eddy as follows:
  — *Infiltration*—water entering the collection system through cracks, joints or breaks.
  — *Steady inflow*—water discharged from cellar and foundation drains, cooling water discharges, and drains from springs and swampy areas. This type of inflow is steady and is identified and measured along with infiltration.
  — *Direct flow*—those types of inflow that have a direct stormwater runoff connection to the sanitary sewer and cause an almost immediate increase in wastewater flows. Possible sources are roof leaders, yard and areaway drains, manhole covers, cross

connections from storm drains and catch basins, and combined sewers.
— *Total inflow*—the sum of the direct inflow at any point in the system plus any flow discharged from the system upstream through overflows, pumping station bypasses, and the like.
— *Delayed inflow*—stormwater that may require several days or more to drain through the sewer system. This category can include the discharge of sump pumps from cellar drainage as well as the slowed entry of surface water through manholes in ponded areas.[5]

* *Influent*—the wastewater entering a tank, channel or treatment process.
* *Inorganic*—mineral materials such as salt, ferric chloride, iron, sand, gravel, etc.
* *License*—a certificate issued by a State Board of Waterworks/ Wastewater Works Operators authorizing the holder to perform the duties of a wastewater treatment plant operator.
* *Mean Cell Residence Time (MCRT)*—the average length of time a mixed liquor suspended solids particle remains in the activated sludge process. May also be known as sludge retention time.
* *mg/L*—an expression of the weight of one substance contained within another. Commonly, it is used to express weight of a substance within a given weight of water or wastewater. It is sometimes expressed as parts per million (ppm), which is equal to mg/L. If there is one pound of a substance mixed in one million pounds, the resulting concentration is 1 mg/L.

$$\text{concentration, mg/L} = \frac{\text{weight of water/wastewater}}{\text{weight of substance} \times 10^6} \qquad (1)$$

* *Mixed liquor*—the combination of return activated sludge and wastewater in the aeration tank.
* *Mixed Liquor Suspended Solids (MLSS)*—the suspended solids concentration of the mixed liquor.
* *Mixed Liquor Volatile Suspended Solids (MLVSS)*—the concentration of organic matter in the mixed liquor suspended solids.
* *Milligrams/Liter (mg/L)*—a measure of concentration. It is equivalent to parts per million (ppm).
* *Moisture content*—the amount of water per unit weight of biosolids. The moisture content is expressed as a percentage of the total weight of the

[5]Metcalf & Eddy, *Wastewater Engineering: Treatment, Disposal, Reuse,* 3rd. ed. New York: Nc-Graw-Hill, Inc., pp. 29–31, 1991.

wet biosolids. This parameter is equal to 100 minus the percent solids concentration.

- *Natural draft*—the negative pressure created by the height of a stack or chimney and the difference in temperature between flue gases and the atmosphere.
- *Nitrogenous Oxygen Demand (NOD)*—a measure of the amount of oxygen required to biologically oxidize nitrogen compounds under specified conditions of time and temperature.
- *NPDES Permit*—National Pollutant Discharge Elimination System permit that authorizes the discharge of treated wastes and specifies the conditions that must be met for discharge.
- *Nutrients*—substances required to support living organisms. Usually refers to nitrogen, phosphorus, iron and other trace metals.
- *Opacity*—the degree of obstruction of light, e.g., a clear glass window has zero opacity, whereas a wall has 100% opacity.
- *Organic*—materials that consist of carbon, hydrogen, oxygen, sulfur, and nitrogen. Many organics are biologically degradable. All organic compounds can be converted to carbon dioxide and water when subjected to high temperatures.
- *Particulate matter*—any material, except water in uncombined form, that is or has been airborne and exists as a liquid or a solid at standard temperatures.
- *Pathogenic*—disease causing. A pathogenic organism is capable of causing illness.
- *Point Source*—any discernible, defined and discrete location or conveyance from which pollutants are or may be discharged.
- *Parts per million (ppm)*—an alternative (but numerically equivalent) to the unit used in chemistry, namely, milligrams per liter (mg/L). As an analogy, think of a ppm unit as equivalent to a full shot glass in a standard swimming pool.
- *Pyrolysis*—the chemical decomposition of organic matter through the application of heat in an oxygen-deficient atmosphere.
- *Return Activated Sludge Solids (RASS)*—the concentration of suspended solids in the sludge flow being returned from the settling tank to the head of the aeration tank.
- *Sanitary wastewater*—wastes discharged from residences and commercial, institutional, and similar facilities that generate both sewage and industrial wastes.
- *Scrubbing*—the removal of impurities from a gas stream by spraying of a liquid.
- *Scum*—the mixture of floatable solids and water removed from the surface of a settling tank.

- *Septic*—a wastewater that has no dissolved oxygen present. It is generally characterized by black color and rotten egg (hydrogen sulfide) odors.
- *Settleability*—a process-control test used to evaluate the settling characteristics of activated sludge. Readings taken at 30 to 60 minutes are used to calculate the settled sludge volume (SSV) and the sludge volume index (SVI).
- *Settled Sludge Volume*—the volume in percent occupied by an activated sludge sample after 30 to 60 minutes of settling. Normally written as SSV with a subscript to indicate the time of the reading used for calculation (SSV_{60}) or (SSV_{30}).
- *Sewage*—wastewater containing human wastes.
- *Slagging*—the destructive chemical action that forms slag on refractory materials subjected to high temperatures; also molten or viscous coating produced on refractory materials by ash particles.
- *Sludge*—the mixture of settleable solids and water that is removed from the bottom of the settling tank.
- *Sludge loading rate*—the weight of wet biosolids fed to the reactor per square foot of reactor bed area per hour ($lb/ft^2/h$).
- *Sludge Retention Time (SRT)*—see Mean Cell Residence Time.
- *Sludge Volume Index (SVI)*—a process-control calculation used to evaluate the settling quality of activated sludge. Requires SSV_{30} and mixed liquor suspended solids test results to calculate.
- *Solids concentration*—the weight of solids per unit weight of sludge.
- *Solids content*—also called percent total solids, is the weight of total solids in biosolids per unit total weight of biosolids expressed in percent. Water content plus solids content equals 100%. This includes all chemicals and other solids added to the biosolids.
- *Solids feed rate*—the dry solids fed to a centrifuge.
- *Solids loading (belt filter press)*—the feed solids to the belt filter on a dry weight basis including chemicals per unit time.
- *Solids loading rate (drying beds)*—the weight of solids on a dry weight basis applied annually per square foot of drying bed area.
- *Solids recovery (centrifuge)*—the ratio of cake solids to feed solids for equal sampling times. It can be calculated with suspended solids and flow data or with only suspended solids data. The centrate solids must be corrected if chemicals are fed to the centrifuge.
- *Storm sewer*—a collection system designed to carry only stormwater runoff.
- *Stormwater*—runoff resulting from rainfall and snowmelt.
- *Supernatant*—the amber-colored liquid above the sludge in a digester.
- *Thermal efficiency*—the ratio of heat used to total heat generated.

- *Turbulence*—a state of high agitation. In turbulent fluid flow, the velocity of a given particle changes constantly both in magnitude and direction.
- *Volatile*—used to describe any substance that evaporates at low temperature.
- *Volatility*—the ability of a substance to convert into vapor or gas without chemical change.
- *Wastewater*—the water supply of a community after it has been soiled by use.
- *Waste Activated Sludge Solids (WASS)*—the concentration of suspended solids in sludge that is being removed from the activated sludge process.
- *Weir*—a device used to measure wastewater flow.
- *Zoogleal slime*—the biological slime that forms on fixed film treatment devices. It contains a wide variety of organisms essential to the treatment process.

1.5 THE BOTTOM LINE

We've made every attempt to format this presentation in ways that allow you to build on the information we present, step-by-step, page-by-page, as you progress through the material. This text consolidates expert information available in many other sources (see Table 1.1 for a list of useful resources), giving you what you need to know for success as a plant operator and for licensure. For additional information or more specific material on any of the topics presented, you should consult one or more of the references provided in Table 1.1.

No one can guarantee that you will pass a state licensure examination. However, we've made every effort to include in this text the type of information that will help you learn the information you need to know to pass these tests—to increase your knowledge of wastewater operations, your sampling and sample testing knowledge and prepare for licensure. No single text can cover all the areas required, so you must augment the content of this text with other, more in-depth training materials. These materials include the various field study programs available from state water control boards, short courses presented by universities (e.g., Virginia Tech) and/or technical schools, and correspondence studies from such sources as California State University, Sacramento (The "Sacramento Manuals").

The bottom line: Changes in technology and regulations occur frequently in the water pollution control industry. Because of this, it is important, as an operator and/or licensure candidate, to stay attuned to these changes. Wastewater Treatment Plant Operations Made Easy is designed to provide the tune up.

TABLE 1.1. Recommended Reference Material.

1. *Advanced Waste Treatment, A Field Study Program,* 2nd ed., Kerri, K., et al. California State University, Sacramento, CA.

2. *Aerobic Biological Wastewater Treatment Facilities,* Environmental Protection Agency, EPA 430/9-77-006, Washington, D.C., 1977.

3. *Anaerobic Sludge Digestion,* Environmental Protection Agency, EPA 430/9-76-001, Washington, D.C., 1977.

4. *Annual Book of ASTM Standards, Section 11, "Water and Environmental Technology,"* American Society for Testing Materials (ASTM), Philadelphia, PA.

5. *Guidelines Establishing Test Procedures for the Analysis of Pollutants.* Federal Register (40 CFR 136), April 4, 1995 Volume 60, No. 64, Page 17160.

6. *Handbook of Water Analysis,* 2nd ed., HACH Chemical Company, P.O. Box 389, Loveland, CO, 1992.

7. *Industrial Waste Treatment, A Field Study Program, Volume I,* Kerri, K. et al. California State University, Sacramento, CA.

8. *Industrial Waste Treatment, A Field Study Program, Volume 2,* Kerri, K. et al. California State University, Sacramento, CA.

9. *Methods for Chemical Analysis of Water and Wastes,* U.S. Environmental Protection Agency, Environmental Monitoring Systems Laboratory-Cincinnati (EMSL-CL), EPA-6000/4-79-020, Revised March 1983 and 1979 (where applicable).

10. *O & M of Trickling Filters, RBC and Related Processes, Manual of Practice OM-10,* Water Pollution Control Federation (now called Water Environment Federation), Alexandria, VA, 1988.

11. *Operation of Wastewater Treatment Plants, A Field Study Program, Volume I,* 4th ed., Kerri, K., et al. California State University, Sacramento, CA.

12. *Operation of Wastewater Treatment Plants, A Field Study Program, Volume II,* 4th ed., Kerri, K., et al. California State University, Sacramento, CA.

13. *Standard Methods for the Examination of Water and Wastewater,* 18th ed., American Public Health Association, American Water Works Association-Water Environment Federation, Washington, D.C., 1992.

14. *Treatment of Metal Wastestreams,* K. Kerri, et. al., California State University, Sacramento, CA.

15. *Basic Math Concepts: For Water and Wastewater Plant Operators.* Joanne K. Price, Lancaster, PA: Technomic Publishing Company, 1991.

16. *Simplified Wastewater Treatment Plant Operations.* Edward J. Haller, Lancaster, PA: Technomic Publishing Company, 1995.

17. *Wastewater Treatment Plants: Planning, Design, and Operation.* Syed R. Qasim, Lancaster, PA: Technomic Publishing Company, 1994.

18. *Spellman's Standard Handbook for Wastewater Operators, Vols 1, 2, & 3.* Lancaster, PA: Technomic Publishing Company, 1999.

19. *Microbiology for Water/Wastewater Operators.* Spellman, F.R., Lancaster, PA: Technomic Publishing Company, Inc., 1997.

20. *Incinerating Biosolids.* Spellman, F.R., Lancaster, PA: Technomic Publishing Company, Inc., 1997.

21. *Dewatering Biosolids.* Spellman, F.R., Lancaster, PA: Technomic Publishing Company, Inc., 1997.

1.6 CHAPTER 1 SELF-TEST

Matching exercise: Match the definitions listed in part A with the terms listed in part B by placing the correct letter in the blank.

✓ *Note:* After completing this exercise, check your answers with those provided in Appendix A.

Part A:

(1) Describes any substance that evaporates at low temperature _____.

(2) The amount of chemically oxidizable materials present in wastewater _____.

(3) Nitrogen, phosphorus, and other trace metals _____.

(4) Another name for a wastewater lift station _____.

(5) This type of inflow is steady and is identified and measured along with infiltration _____.

(6) Iron, sand, and gravel, etc. _____.

(7) Another name for sludge _____.

(8) Used to describe organisms that function in the absence of oxygen _____.

(9) The suspended solids concentration of mixed liquor _____.

(10) Solid organic matter recovered from a sewage treatment process and used especially as a soil conditioner _____.

(11) Wastewater that has no dissolved oxygen present _____.

(12) Runoff resulting from rainfall and snowmelt _____.

(13) Free oxygen dissolved in water _____.

(14) Heavy inorganic solids, such as sand, gravel, egg shells, or metal filings _____.

(15) The solids formed when microorganisms are used to treat wastewater using the activated sludge process _____.

(16) Process-control calculations used to evaluate settling quality of activated sludge _____.

(17) Conditions in which no free, elemental oxygen is present _____.

(18) Wastewater treatment plant discharge _____.

(19) Contains human wastes _____.

(20) Pollutant discharge from a discernible, defined, and discrete conveyance _____.

(21) Common to fixed film treatment devices _____.

(22) Shreds solids into smaller, less harmful particles _____.

(23) Wastes discharged from residences _____.

(24) Type of bacteria found in bodily discharges of warm-blooded animals
_____.

(25) A type of bacteria used to indicate possible human or animal contamination of water _____.

(26) The highest allowable values for a daily discharge _____.

Part B:

a. septic
b. coliform
c. anaerobic
d. inorganic
e. dissolved oxygen
f. sewage
g. point source
h. effluent
i. nutrients
j. stormwater
k. grit
l. pumping stations
m. mixed liquor suspended solids (MLSS)
n. sludge
o. sanitary wastewater
p. zoogleal slime
q. biosolids
r. activated sludge
s. fecal coliform
t. daily maximum discharge
u. sludge volume index (SVI)
v. steady flow
w. comminution
x. anoxic
y. chemical oxygen demand
z. volatile

CHAPTER 2

Wastewater Math

To properly operate a wastewater treatment plant and to pass the examination for a wastewater operator's license, you must know how to do certain calculations.

2.1 BASIC MATH

WHETHER in a made-easy format or some other format, without the ability to perform basic mathematical calculations wastewater plant operators would have difficulty in maintaining proper plant operations and in passing licensure exams. In reality, however, most of the calculations required to be performed by the operator are not that difficult. For those operators who fear math, we refer you to worthy advice given by J.K. Price:

"Those who have difficulty in math often do not lack the ability for mathematical calculation, they merely have not learned, or have been taught, the "language of math."

As Price points out, mathematics is a *language*—a universal language. Mathematical symbols have the same meaning to people speaking many different languages throughout the world. The language of mathematics consists of symbols, definitions, and math terms.

In this chapter we review the basics and introduce those math concepts believed to be critical and minimum conditions for the "Qualified Operator".

2.2 CALCULATION STEPS

Many methods can be successfully used to solve wastewater math problems. One of the standard methods of math problem solving is listed as follows:

[6]Price, J. K., *Applied Math for Wastewater Plant Operator.* Lancaster, PA: Technomic Publishing Company, p. vii, 1991.

(1) If appropriate, make a drawing of the information in the problem.

(2) Place the given data on the drawing.

(3) Determine "What is the question?" This is the first thing you should ask as you begin to solve the problem, along with: "What are they really looking for?" Writing down exactly what is being looked for is always smart. Sometimes the answer has more than one unknown. For instance, you may need to find "X" then find "Y."

(4) If the calculation calls for an equation, write it down.

(5) Fill in the data in the equation and look to see what is missing.

(6) Rearrange or transpose the equation, if necessary.

(7) If available, use a calculator.

(8) Always write down the answer.

(9) Check any solution obtained.

For some people, straightforward math such as addition, subtraction, multiplication, division and other operations that are listed with numerical values are usually easier to solve than are word problems. However, certain key words aid in solving word problems. For example, the word "of" means multiply, "and" means add, "per" means divide, and "less than" means subtract.

2.3 SEQUENCE OF OPERATIONS

In a series of additions, the terms may be placed in any order and grouped in any way. Thus, $4 + 2 = 6$ and $2 + 4 = 6$; $(2 + 3) + (6 + 4) = 15$, $(6 + 2) + (3 + 4) = 15$, and $[5 + (3 + 4)] + 3 = 15$.

In a series of subtractions, changing the order or the grouping of the terms may change the result. Thus, $100 - 20 = 80$, but $20 - 100 = -80$; $(100 - 10) - 10 = 80$, but $100 - (10 - 10) = 100$.

When no grouping is given, the subtractions are performed in the order written, from left to right. Thus, $100 - 30 - 15 - 4 = 51$; or, by steps, $100 - 30 = 70$, $70 - 15 = 55$, $55 - 4 = 51$.

In a series of multiplications, the factors may be placed in any order and in any grouping. Thus, $[(2 \times 3) \times 5] \times 6 = 180$ and $5 \times [2 \times (6 \times 3)] = 180$.

In a series of divisions, changing the order or the grouping may change the result. Thus, $100 \div 10 = 10$, but $10 \div 100 = 0.1$; $(100 \div 10) \div 2 = 5$, but $100 \div (10 \div 2) = 20$. Again, if no grouping is indicated, the divisions are performed in the order written, from left to right. Thus, $100 \div 10 \div 2$ is understood to mean $(100 \div 10) \div 2$.

In a series of mixed mathematical operations, the convention is as follows: whenever no grouping is given, multiplications and divisions are to be performed in the order written, then additions and subtractions in the order written.

Example 2.1

$$12 + 2 + 3 - 4 - 2 + 6 - 3 - 3 = 11$$

By performing operations in the order in which they are given.

Example 2.2

$$120 \div 2 \times 50 \times 2 \div 2 = 3000$$

Example 2.3

$$(12 \div 3) + (8 \times 2) - (6 \div 2) + (7 \times 2 \times 3) - 9 = 50$$

First perform the multiplications and divisions, then the additions and subtractions.

✓ *Note:* An easier way to complete Example 2.3 is indicated as follows:

$$(12 \div 3) + (8 \times 2) - (6 \div 2) + (7 \times 2 \times 3) - 9 =$$
$$4 \quad + \quad 16 \quad - \quad 3 \quad + \quad 42 \quad - 9 = 50$$

Again, first perform the multiplications and divisions, then the additions and subtractions.

Example 2.4

In a series of different operations, parentheses ( ) and brackets [ ] can be used to group the operations in the desired order. Thus, $120 \div 3 \times 5 \times 2 \div 2 = \{[(120 \div 3)5]2\} \div 2 = 200$

2.4 FRACTIONS

The number 6 divided by 3 gives an exact quotient of 2. This may be written 6/3 = 2. However, if you attempt to divide 6 by 9, you are unable to calculate an exact quotient. This division may be written 6/9 (read "six-ninths"). The number 6/9 represents a number, but not a whole number. This is called a fraction. Simply put, fractions are used to express a portion of a whole.

Wastewater operators are often faced with routine situations that require thinking in fractions, and on occasion, actually working with fractions. One of the common uses for the rules governing the use of fractions in a math problem is dealing with units of the problem. Units like gpm are actually fractions, gallons per minute or gal/min and cubic feet per second or cfs is actually ft³/sec. As you can see, understanding fractions helps in solving other problems.

A fraction is composed of three items, two numbers and a line. The number on the top is called the *numerator*, the number on the bottom is called the *denominator* and the line in between them means divide.

$$\text{Divide } \quad \frac{4}{5} \quad \begin{array}{l} \leftarrow \text{ Numerator} \\ \leftarrow \text{ Denominator} \end{array}$$

The denominator indicates the number of equal-sized pieces the whole "thing" has been cut into. The numerator tells how many pieces there are. For example, the circle in Figure 2.1 has been divided into four equal pieces, so the denominator will be 4. Each single piece represents 1/4 of the circle. Three of the pieces are shaded, representing 3/4 of the circle.

2.4.1 FRACTIONS: PRINCIPLES

Like all other math functions, how we deal with fractions is governed by rules or principles. The following is a discussion of the principles associated with using fractions.

(1) *Same numerator and denominator:* When the numerator and denominator of a fraction are the same, the fraction can be reduced to 1. For example:

$$\frac{5}{5} = 1, \quad \frac{31}{31} = 1, \quad \frac{69}{69} = 1, \quad \frac{12}{12} = 1, \quad \frac{169}{169} = 1$$

(2) *Whole numbers to fractions:* Any whole number can be expressed as a fraction by placing a "1" in the denominator. For example:

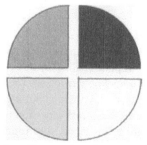

Figure 2.1. An example of fractions. There are four pieces, so each piece is 1/4. The three shaded pieces represent 3/4.

5 is the same as $\dfrac{5}{1}$, and 69 is the same as $\dfrac{69}{1}$

(3) *Adding Fractions:* Only fractions with the same denominator can be added, and only the numerators are added. The denominator stays the same. For example:

$$\frac{2}{8}+\frac{3}{8}=\frac{5}{8}, \text{ and } \frac{3}{9}+\frac{4}{9}=\frac{7}{9}$$

(4) *Subtracting Fractions:* Only fractions with the same denominator can be subtracted, and only the numerators are subtracted. The denominator remains the same. For example:

$$\frac{7}{9}-\frac{4}{9}=\frac{3}{9}, \text{ and } \frac{16}{30}-\frac{12}{30}=\frac{4}{30}$$

(5) *Mixed Numbers:* A fraction combined with a whole number is called a mixed number. For example:

$$3\frac{1}{3}, \quad 14\frac{2}{7}, \quad 6\frac{3}{5}, \quad 40\frac{1}{3}, \quad 21\frac{13}{31}$$

These numbers are read, "three and one third," "fourteen and two sevenths," "6 and three fifths," "40 and one third," and "twenty-one and thirteen thirty ones."

(6) *Changing a Fraction:* A fraction is changed by multiplying the numerator and the denominator by the same number, which does not change the value of the fraction. For instance:

$$\frac{1}{4} \text{ is the same as } \frac{1\times4}{4\times4} \text{ which is } \frac{4}{16}$$

(7) *Simplest Terms:* Fractions should be reduced to their simplest terms by dividing the numerator and denominator by the same number. The result of this division must leave both the numerator and the denominator as whole numbers. For instance:

$$\frac{3}{6} \text{ is not in its simplest terms, by dividing both by 3 we obtain } \frac{1}{2}$$

The number 2/3 cannot be reduced any further since there is no number that can be divided evenly into the 2 and the 3.

Example 2.5

Problem:

Reduce the following to their simplest terms.

$$\frac{2}{4}= \qquad \frac{14}{18}= \qquad \frac{3}{4}= \qquad \frac{6}{10}= \qquad \frac{9}{18}= \qquad \frac{17}{29}= \qquad \frac{24}{32}=$$

Solutions:

$$\frac{2}{4}=\frac{1}{2} \qquad \text{both were divided by 2}$$

$$\frac{14}{18}=\frac{7}{9} \qquad \text{both were divided by 2}$$

$$\frac{3}{4}=\frac{3}{4} \qquad \text{in its simplest terms}$$

$$\frac{6}{10}=\frac{3}{5} \qquad \text{both were divided by 2}$$

$$\frac{9}{18}=\frac{1}{2} \qquad \text{both were divided by 9}$$

$$\frac{17}{29}=\frac{17}{29} \qquad \text{in its simplest terms}$$

$$\frac{24}{32}=\frac{3}{4} \qquad \text{both were divided by 8}$$

(8) *Reducing Even Numbers:* When the starting point is not obvious, do the following: If the numerator and denominator are both even numbers (2, 4, 6, 8, 10, etc), divide them both by 2, continue dividing by 2 until a division will no longer yield a whole number with the numerator and denominator.

(9) *Reducing Odd Numbers:* When the numerator and denominator are both odd numbers (3, 5, 7, 9, 11, 13, 15, 17), attempt to divide by three, continue dividing by 3 until a division will no longer yield a whole number with the numerator and denominator. It is obvious that some numbers such as 5, 7 and 11 cannot be divided by 3 and may in fact be in their simplest terms.

(10) *Different Denominators:* To add and/or subtract fractions with different denominators, the denominators must be changed to a common denominator. The denominators must be the same before adding or subtracting the fraction. One of the simplest methods of obtaining a common denominator is to multiply the denominators. Each fraction must then be converted to a fraction expressing the new denominator.

For instance to add 1/8 and 2/5 together:

- Start by multiplying the denominators 8 × 5 = 40
- Change 1/8 to a fraction with 40 as the denominator 40/8 = 5, 5 × 1 = 5 (the numerator), new fraction is 5/40

Notice that this is the same as 1/8 except 5/40 is not reduced to its simplest terms. Change 2/5 to a fraction with 40 as the denominator 40/5 = 8, 8 × 2 = 16 (the numerator), new fraction is 16/40

- Complete the addition

$$\frac{5}{40} + \frac{16}{40} = \frac{21}{40}$$

(11) *Numerator Larger:* Any time the numerator is larger than the denominator, the fraction should be turned into a mixed number. This is accomplished by the following procedure:

- Determine the number of times the denominator can be divided evenly into the numerator. This will be the whole number portion of the mixed number.
- Multiply the whole number times the denominator and subtract from the numerator. This value (the remainder) becomes the numerator of the fraction portion of the mixed number.

$$\frac{28}{12}, \text{ is divisible by 12 twice, 2 is the whole number}$$

$$2 \times 12 = 24$$

$$\frac{28}{12} - \frac{24}{12} = \frac{4}{12}, \text{ dividing top and bottom by 4} = \frac{1}{3}$$

$$\text{New mixed number is } 2\frac{1}{3}$$

(12) *Multiplying Fractions:* To multiply fractions, simply multiply the numerators and denominators, then reduce to the simplest terms. For instance: Find the result of multiplying $1/8 \times 2/3$

$$\frac{1}{8} \times \frac{2}{3} = \frac{1 \times 2 = 2}{8 \times 3 = 24} = \frac{2}{24} = \frac{1}{12}$$

(13) *Dividing Fractions:* To divide fractions, simply invert the denominator (turn it upside down), multiply, and reduce to simplest terms. For example:

Divide 1/9 by 2/3

$$\frac{\frac{1}{9}}{\frac{2}{3}} = \frac{1}{9} \times \frac{3}{2} = \frac{1 \times 3 = 3}{9 \times 2 = 18} = \frac{3}{18}, \text{ reduced} = \frac{1}{6}$$

✓ *Note:* The divide symbol can be ÷ or / or —.

(14) *Fractions to Decimals:* To convert a fraction to a decimal, simply divide the numerator by the denominator. For example:

$$\frac{1}{2} = 0.5, \quad \frac{5}{8} = 0.625, \quad \frac{7}{16} = 0.4375, \quad \frac{1}{4} = 0.25$$

(15) *Change Inches to Feet:* To change inches to feet, divide the number of inches by 12. For example:

Change 5 inches to feet

$$\frac{5}{12} = 0.42 \text{ feet}$$

Example 2.6

Change the following to feet: 2 inches, 3 inches, 4 inches, 8 inches

$$\frac{2}{12} = 0.167 \text{ feet} \qquad \frac{3}{12} = 0.25 \text{ feet}$$

$$\frac{4}{12} = 0.33 \text{ feet} \qquad \frac{8}{12} = 0.667 \text{ feet}$$

2.5 DECIMALS

While we often use fractions when dealing with measurements, dealing with decimals is often easier when we do calculations, especially when working with pocket calculators and computers.

A decimal is composed of two sets of numbers. The numbers to the left of the decimal are whole numbers, and numbers to the right of the decimal are parts of whole numbers, a fraction of a number.

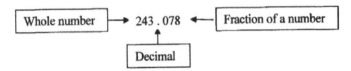

The term used to denote the fraction component is dependent on the number of characters to the right of the decimal (see Figure 2.2). Insert Figure 2.2 Values of positions.

The first character after the decimal point is tenths; the second character is hundredths; the third is thousandths; the fourth is ten thousandths; and the fifth is hundred thousandths.

- 0.1—tenths
- 0.01—hundredths
- 0.001—thousandths
- 0.0001—ten thousandths
- 0.00001—hundred thousandths

When we use a calculator, we can convert a fraction to a decimal by dividing.

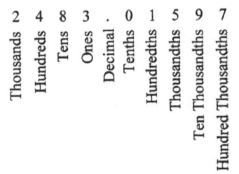

Figure 2.2. Values of positions.

26 WASTEWATER MATH

The horizontal line or diagonal line of the fraction indicates that we divide the bottom number into the top number.

For example, to convert 4/5 to a decimal, we divide 4 by 5. Using a pocket calculator, enter the following keystrokes:

$$4 \div 5 =$$

The display will show the answer, 0.8.

Example 2.7

To determine the amount of chemical solution remaining in a circular mixing tank, we need to determine the volume of the liquid in the tank in cubic feet. Since the volume is equal to the surface area of the liquid times the depth of the liquid, we measure the tank and find it has a diameter of 2 feet, 8 inches, and the liquid is 1 foot, 5 inches deep. We cannot multiply mixed dimensions like feet-and-inches, so before we can proceed with the calculations, we must convert the feet-and-inches measurements to feet-and-decimals-of-a-foot. We first state the dimensions as feet-and-fractions-of-a-foot by stating the inches as a fraction of a foot. There are 12 inches in a foot, so 8 inches is 8/12 of a foot: the diameter is 2 feet and 8/12 of a foot, and the liquid depth is 1 foot and 5/12 of a foot. Doing the division of the fractions, we find that 8/12 of a foot is 0.67 ft and 5/12 of a foot is 0.42 ft. The diameter is 2.67 ft, and the depth is 1.42 ft. We can then proceed with the volume calculation.

When a calculator is not available, operators often cannot remember the basic rules associated with working with decimals. Therefore, we provide a brief review.

As mentioned, when a number is less than one and is expressed as a decimal, we place a "0" (zero) to the left of the decimal. This makes it clear that the number is less than one. For instance, 0.33 is much clearer than .33.

2.5.1 DECIMAL OPERATIONS

2.5.1.1 Subtracting Decimals

When subtracting decimals, simply line up the numbers at the decimal and subtract. For example:

$$
\begin{array}{r}
24.65 \\
-13.64 \\
\hline
11.01
\end{array}
\qquad
\begin{array}{r}
157.700 \\
-14.555 \\
\hline
143.145
\end{array}
$$

2.5.1.2 Adding Decimals

To add numbers with a decimal, use the same rules as subtraction: line up the numbers at the decimal and add.

$$\begin{array}{r} 24.55 \\ +14.98 \\ \hline 39.53 \end{array} \qquad \begin{array}{r} 151.800 \\ +12.666 \\ \hline 164.466 \end{array}$$

2.5.1.3 Multiplying Decimals

To multiply two or more numbers containing decimals, follow these basic steps:

- Multiply the numbers as whole numbers, do not worry about the decimals
- Write down the answer
- Count the total number of digits (numbers) to the right of the decimal in all of the numbers being multiplied.

For example, multiplying 3.55×8.4 yields the number 29820. There are a total of three digits to the right of the decimal point (2 for the number 3.55 and 1 for the number 8.4). Therefore, the decimal point would be placed three places to the left from the right of the 0.

$$29.820$$

2.5.1.4 Dividing Decimals

To divide a number by a number containing a decimal, the divisor must be made into a whole number by moving the decimal point to the right until we have a whole number.

- Count the number of places the decimal needed to be moved.
- Move the decimal in the dividend by the same number of places.

2.6 ROUNDING NUMBERS

Numbers are rounded to reduce the number of digits to the right of the decimal point. This is for convenience, not accuracy.

✓ *Note:* A number is rounded off by dropping one or more numbers from the right and adding zeros if necessary to place the decimal point. If the last figure dropped is 5 or more, increase the last retained figure by 1. If the last digit dropped is less than 5, do not increase the last retained figure.

Example 2.8

Problem:

Round off 10,546 to 4, 3, 2, and 1 significant figures.

Solution:

$$10,546 = 10,550 \text{ to 4 significant figures}$$
$$10,546 = 10,500 \text{ to 3 significant figures}$$
$$10,547 = 11,000 \text{ to 2 significant figures}$$
$$10,547 = 10,000 \text{ to 1 significant figure}$$

2.7 DETERMINING SIGNIFICANT FIGURES

The concept of significant figures is related to rounding. It can be used to determine where to round off. The basic idea is that no answer can be more accurate than the least accurate piece of data used to calculate the answer.

✓ *Note:* Significant figures are those numbers, which are known to be reliable. The position of the decimal point does not determine the number of significant figures.

Example 2.9

Problem:

How many significant figures are there in a measurement of 1.45 in?

Solution:

There are three significant figures: 1, 4, and 5.

Example 2.10

Problem:

How many significant figures are there in a measurement of 0.000145?

Solution:

There are again three significant figures: 1, 4, and 5. The three zeros are used only to place the decimal point.

Example 2.11

Problem:

How many significant figures are there in a measurement of 107,500?

Solution:

There are four significant figures: 1, 0, 7, and 5. The remaining two zeros are used to place the decimal point.

Example 2.12

Problem:

How many significant figures are in 29,000.0?

Solution:

There are six significant figures: 2, 9, 0, 0, 0, 0. In this case, the .0 means that the measurement is precise to 1/10 unit. The zeros indicate measured values and are not used solely to place the decimal point.

2.8 POWERS

Powers are used to identify area in square feet, and volume as in cubic feet. Powers can also be used to indicate that a number should be squared, cubed, etc. This later designation is the number of times a number must be multiplied times itself.

More specifically, when several numbers are multiplied together, as $2 \times 3 \times 4 = 24$, the numbers 2, 3, and 4 are the *factors;* 24 is the *product.* If all the factors are alike, as $2 \times 2 \times 2 \times 2 = 16$, the product is called a *power.* Thus, 16 is a power of 2, and 2 is the *base* of the power. A power is a product obtained repeating the same base a certain number of times as a factor.

Instead of writing $2 \times 2 \times 2 \times 2$, it is more convenient to use an *exponent* to indicate that the factor 2 is used as a factor four times. This exponent (a small number placed above and to the right of the base number) indicates how many times the base is to be used as a factor. Using this system of notation, the multiplication $2 \times 2 \times 2 \times 2$ is written as 2^4. The 4 is the exponent, showing that 2 is to be used as a factor four times.

Example 2.13

Problem:

Rewrite $10 \times 10 \times 10$ and calculate the product.

Solution:

$$10 \times 10 \times 10 = 10^3 = 1,000$$

Example 2.14

Problem:

Rewrite $2 \times 2 \times 2 \times 2 \times 2$ and calculate the product.

Solution:

$$2 \times 2 \times 2 \times 2 \times 2 = 2^5 = 32$$

Example 2.15

Problem:

Rewrite $3 \times 3 \times 4 \times 4 \times 4$ and compute the product.

Solution:

$$3 \times 3 \times 4 \times 4 \times 4 = 3^2 \times 4^3 = 9 \times 64 = 576$$

Example 2.16

Problem:

What is 12 cubed? 12 squared?

Solution:

$$12 \text{ cubed} = 12^3 = 12 \times 12 \times 12 = 1{,}728$$
$$12 \text{ squared} = 12^2 = 12 \times 12 = 144$$

2.9 AVERAGES

An average is a way of representing several different measurements as a single number. Although averages can be useful by telling "about" how much of how many, they can also be misleading, as we demonstrate below. You find two kinds of averages in wastewater calculations: the arithmetic mean (or, simply, "mean") and the median.

✓ *Note:* The mean (what we usually refer to as an average) is the total of values of a set of observations divided by the number of observations. We simply add up all of the individual measurements and divide by the total number of measurements we took.

Example 2.17

Problem:

A wastewater operator takes a chlorine residual measurement every day. We show part of (one week) the operating log below.

Daily Chlorine Residual Results

Day	Chlorine Residual (mg/l)
Monday	0.9
Tuesday	1.0
Wednesday	1.2
Thursday	1.3
Friday	1.4
Saturday	1.1
Sunday	0.9

Find the mean.

Solution:

Add up the seven chlorine residual readings: 0.9 + 1.0 + 1.2 + 1.3 + 1.4

+ 1.1 + 0.9 = 7.8. Next divide by the number of measurements (in this case seven): 7.8 ÷ 7 = 1.11. The mean chlorine residual for the week was 1.11 mg/l.

✓ *Note:* The *median* is simply defined as the value of the central item when the data are arrayed or ranked by size. First, arrange all of the readings in either ascending or descending order. Then, find the middle value.

Example 2.18

Problem:

In our chlorine residual example, what is the median?

Solution:

Arrange the values in ascending order: 0.9, 0.9, 1.0, 1.1, 1.2, 1.3, 1.4

The middle value is the fourth one—1.1. So, the median chlorine residual is 1.1 mg/l. (Usually, the median will be a different value from the mean).

If the data contains an even number of values, you must add one more step, since no middle value is present. You must find the two values in the middle, and then find the mean of those two values.

Example 2.19

Problem:

A water system has four wells with the following capacities: 110 gpm, 100 gpm, 135 gpm, and 90 gpm. What are the mean and the median pumping capacities?

Solution:

The mean is

$$\frac{110 \text{ gpm} + 100 \text{ gpm} + 135 \text{ gpm} + 90 \text{ gpm}}{4} = \frac{435}{4} = 108.75 \text{ gpm}$$

To find the median, arrange the values in order: 90 gpm, 100 gpm, 110 gpm, 135 gpm

With four values, there is no single "middle" value, so we must take the mean of the two middle values:

$$\frac{100 \text{ gpm} + 110 \text{ gpm}}{2} = 105 \text{ gpm}$$

At times, determining what the original numbers were like is difficult (if not impossible) when dealing only with averages.

Example 2.20

Problem:

A water system has four storage tanks. Three of them have a capacity of 100,000 gallons each, while the fourth has a capacity of 1 million gallons. What is the mean capacity of the storage tanks?

Solution:

The mean capacity of the storage tanks is

$$\frac{100,000 + 100,000 + 100,000 + 1,000,000}{4} = 325,000 \text{ gal}$$

✓ *Note:* Notice that no tank in Example 2.20 has a capacity anywhere close to the mean. The median capacity requires us to take the mean of the two middle values; since they are both 100,000 gal, the median is 100,000 gal. Although three of the tanks have the same capacity as the median, this data offers no indication that one of these tanks holds a million gallons—information that could be important for the operator to know.

2.10 RATIO

One place where fractions are used in calculations is in ratios used to calculate solutions.

Ratio is the comparison of two numbers by division or an indicated division. A ratio is usually stated in the form A is to B as C is to D, and is written as two fractions that are equal to each other:

$$\frac{A}{B} = \frac{C}{D} \tag{2.1}$$

We solve ratio problems by cross-multiplying; that is, we multiply the left numerator (A) by the right denominator (D) and say that (AD) is equal to the left denominator (B) times the right numerator (C; i.e., BC):

$$A \times D = B \times C$$

$$AD = BC$$

(2.2)

If one of the four items is unknown, we solve the ratio by dividing the two known items that are multiplied together by the known item that is multiplied by the unknown. This is best shown by a couple of examples.

Example 2.21

Problem:

If we need 4 pounds of alum to treat 2,000 gallons of water, how many pounds of alum will we need to treat 10,000 gallons?

Solution:

We state this as a ratio: 4 pounds of alum is to 2,000 gallons of water as "pounds of alum" (or x) is to 10,000 gallons." We set this up this way:

$$\frac{4 \text{ lb alum}}{2,000 \text{ gal water}} = \frac{x \text{ lb alum}}{10,000 \text{ gal water}}$$

Cross-multiplying:

$$2,000 \times x = 4 \times 10,000$$

$$x = \frac{4 \times 10,000}{2,000}$$

$$x = 20 \text{ lb alum}$$

Example 2.22

Problem:

If 10 gallons of fuel oil cost $5.00, how much do 16 gallons cost?

Solution:

$$\frac{10 \text{ gal}}{\$5.00} = \frac{16 \text{ gal}}{\$ y}$$

$$10 \times y = 16 \times \$5.00$$

$$= \frac{16 \times \$5.00}{10}$$

$$= \frac{80}{10}$$

$$= \$8.00$$

2.11 PERCENT

Percent (like fractions) is another way of expressing a part of a whole. The term percent means "per hundred," so a percentage is the number out of 100. For example, 22 percent (or 22%) means 22 out of 100 (or 22/100). If we divide 22 by 100, we get the decimal 0.22:

$$22\% = \frac{22}{100} = 0.22$$

When percentages are used in calculations (such as when calculating hypochlorite dosages, and the percent available chlorine must be considered), the percentage must be converted to an equivalent decimal number. Divide the percentage by 100.

Example 2.23

Problem:

Calcium hypochlorite (HTH) contains 65% available chlorine. What is the decimal equivalent of 65%?

Solution:

Since 65% means 65 per hundred, divide 65 by 100: 65/100, which is 0.65.

Decimals and fractions can also be converted to percentages. First convert the fraction to a decimal, then multiply the decimal by 100 to get the percentage. For example, if a 50-foot high water tank has 32 feet of water in it, how full is the tank in terms of the percentage of its capacity?

$$\frac{32 \text{ ft}}{50 \text{ ft}} = 0.64 \text{ [decimal equivalent]}$$

$$0.64 \times 100 = 64\%$$

Thus, the tank is 64% full.

2.12 UNITS AND CONVERSIONS

Most of the calculations made in wastewater operations have units connected with them. While the number tells us how many, the units tell us what we have. Examples of units include inches, feet, square feet, cubic feet, gallons, pounds, milliliters, milligrams per liter, pounds per square inch, miles per hour, and so on.

Conversions are a process of changing the units of a number to make the number usable in a specific instance. Conversions are accomplished by multiplying or dividing into another number to change the units of the number. Common conversions in wastewater operations are as follows:

- gpm to cfs
- million gallons to acre feet
- Cubic feet to acre feet
- Cubic feet of water to weight
- Cubic feet of water to gallons
- Gallons of water to weight
- gpm to MGD (million gallons per day)
- psi to feet of head (the measure of the pressure of water expressed as height of water in feet, 1 psi = 2.31 feet of head).

To understand more clearly how various units are used and how to perform conversions, we illustrate by example. Consider when we add or subtract numbers, the units must be the same. If we add 3 feet to 9 feet, for instance, we get an answer of 12 feet. But if we add 2 feet to 3 yards, we cannot get an answer unless we convert the feet into yards or the yards into feet. Converting larger units to smaller units is usually easier, but the type of conversion may also depend on the answer we want. In our example, we can convert yards into feet by multiplying by 3, because there are 3 feet in one yard; then, we can easily add 2 feet to 9 feet.

$$2 \text{ ft} + (3 \text{ yd} \times 3 \text{ ft/yd}) = 2 \text{ ft} + 9 \text{ ft} = 11 \text{ ft}$$

In many instances, the conversion factor cannot be derived. It must be known.

Therefore, we use tables such as Table 2.1 to determine the common conversions.

✓ *Note:* Conversion factors are used to change measurements or calculated values from one unit of measure to another. In making the conversion from one unit to another, you must know two things: (1) The exact number that relates the two units and (2) Whether to multiply or divide by that number.

TABLE 2.1. Conversion Table.

To Convert	Multiply By	To Get
Feet	12	Inches
Yards	3	Feet
Yards	36	Inches
Inches	2.54	Centimeters
Meters	3.3	Feet
Meters	100	Centimeters
Meters	1,000	Millimeters
Square Yards	9	Square Feet
Square Feet	144	Square Inches
Acres	43,560	Square Feet
Cubic Yards	27	Cubic Feet
Cubic Feet	1,728	Cubic Inches
Cubic Feet (Water)	7.48	Gallons
Cubic Feet (Water)	62.4	Pounds
Acre Feet	43,500	Cubic Feet
Gallons (Water)	8.34	Pounds
Gallons (Water)	3,785	Liters
Gallons (Water)	3,785	Milliliters
Gallons (Water)	3,785	Cubic Centimeters
Gallons (Water)	3,785	Grams
Liters	1,000	Milliliters
Days	24	Hours
Days	1,440	Minutes
Days	86,400	Seconds
Million Gallons/Day	1,000,000	Gallons/Day
Million Gallons/Day	694.4	Gallons/Day
Million Gallons/Day	1.55	Cubic Feet/Second
Million Gallons/Day	3.069	Acre Feet/Day
Million Gallons/Day	36.8	Acre Inches/Day
Million Gallons/Day	3,785	Cubic Meters/Day
Gallons/Minute	1,440	Gallons/Day
Gallons/Minute	3.785	Liters/Minute
Pounds	454	Grams
Grams	1,000	Milligrams
Pressure, PSI	2.31	Head, ft (Water)
Horsepower	33,000	Foot Pounds/Minute
Horsepower	0.746	Kilowatts
To Get	Divide by	To Convert

For example, in converting from inches to feet, you must know that there are 12 in. in 1 ft, and you must know whether to multiply or divide the number of inches by 0.08333 (i.e., 1 in. or 0.08 ft).

When making conversions, confusion often occurs over whether to multiply or divide; on the other hand, the number that relates the two units is usually known and thus is not a problem. In order to gain understanding of the proper methodology, the "mechanics" to use for various operations, requires practice.

We provide examples of the types of conversions wastewater operators must be familiar with in the following sections.

Most operators memorize some standard conversions. This happens as a result of using the conversions, not as a result of attempting to memorize them.

✓ *Note*: To convert in the opposite direction (i.e., inches to feet) divide by the factor rather than multiply.

2.12.1 MAKING CONVERSIONS

In the sections to follow, several conversion problems common to wastewater treatment practice are presented.

2.12.1.1 Cubic Feet to Gallons

$$\text{gallons} = \text{cubic feet, ft}^3 \times \text{gal/ft}^3 \qquad\qquad (2.3)$$

Example 2.24

Problem:

How many gallons of sludge can be pumped to a digester that has 3,000 cubic feet of volume available?

Solution:

$$\text{gallons} = 3{,}000\ \text{ft}^3 \times 7.48\ \text{gal/ft}^3 = 22{,}440\ \text{gallons}$$

2.12.1.2 Gallons to Cubic Feet

$$\text{Cubic Feet} = \frac{\text{gallons}}{7.48\ \text{gallons/ft}^3} \qquad\qquad (2.4)$$

Example 2.25

Problem:

How many cubic feet of sludge are removed when 15,000 gallons are withdrawn?

Solution:

$$\text{Cubic Feet} = \frac{15,000 \text{ gallons}}{7.48 \text{ gallons/ft}^3} = 2,005 \text{ ft}^3$$

2.12.1.3 Gallons to Pounds

$$\text{lb} = \text{gallons} \times 8.34 \text{ lb/gal} \qquad (2.5)$$

Example 2.26

Problem:

If 1,400 gal of solids are removed from the primary settling tank, how many pounds of solids are removed?

Solution:

$$\text{lb} = 1,400 \text{ gallons} \times 8.34 \text{ lb/gal} = 11,676 \text{ lb}$$

2.12.1.4 Pounds to Gallons

$$\text{gallons} = \frac{\text{pounds}}{8.34 \text{ lb/gal}} \qquad (2.6)$$

Example 2.27

Problem:

How many gallons of water are required to fill a tank that holds 6,000 lb of water?

Solution:

$$\text{gallons} = \frac{6,000 \text{ lb}}{8.34 \text{ lb/gal}} = 719.4 \text{ gal}$$

2.12.1.5 Milligram/Liter to Pounds

✓ *Note*: For plant control operations, concentrations in milligrams per liter or parts per million determined by laboratory testing must be converted to quantities in pounds, kilogram, pounds per day or kilograms per day.

$$\text{lb} = \text{concentration, mg/L} \times \text{vol., MG} \times 8.34 \text{ lb/mg/L/MG} \qquad (2.7)$$

Example 2.28

Problem:

The solids concentration in the aeration tank is 2400 mg/L. The aeration tank volume is 0.95 MG. How many pounds of solids are in the tank?

Solution:

$$\text{lb} = 2,400 \text{ mg/L} \times 0.95 \text{ MG} \times 8.34 \text{ lb/mg/L/MG} = 19,015 \text{ lb}$$

2.12.1.6 Milligrams per Liter to Pounds per day

$$\text{lb/day} = \text{Conc., mg/L} \times \text{Flow, MGD} \times 8.34 \text{ lb/mg/L/MG} \qquad (2.8)$$

Example 2.29

Problem:

How many pounds of solids are discharged per day when the plant effluent flow rate is 4.55 MGD and the effluent solids concentration is 26 mg/L?

Solution:

$$\text{lb/day} = 26 \text{ mg/L} \times 4.55 \text{ MGD} \times 8.34 \text{ lb/mg/L/MG} = 987 \text{ lb/day}$$

2.12.1.7 Milligrams per Liter to Kilograms per Day

$$\text{kg/day} = \text{conc., mg/L} \times \text{vol., MG} \times 3.785 \text{ dg/mg/L/MG} \qquad (2.9)$$

Example 2.30

Problem:

The effluent contains 35 mg/L of BOD_5. How many kilograms per day of BOD_5 are discharged when the effluent flow rate is 8.5 MGD?

Solution:

$$kg/day = 35 \ mg/L \times 8.5 \ MG \times 3.785 \ dg/mg/L/MG = 1,126 \ kg/day$$

2.12.1.8 Pounds to Milligrams per Liter

$$concentration, \ mg/L = \frac{quantity, \ lb}{vol., \ MG \times 8.34 \ lb/mg/L/MG} \qquad (2.10)$$

Example 2.31

Problem:

The aeration tank contains 79,990 pounds of solids. The volume of the aeration tank is 4.00 MG. What is the concentration of solids in the aeration tank in mg/L?

Solution:

$$concentration, \ mg/L = \frac{79,990 \ lb}{4.00 \ MG \times 8.34 \ lb/mg/L/MG} = 2,398 \ mg/L$$

2.12.1.9 Pounds per Day to Milligrams per Liter

$$conc., \ mg/L = \frac{quantity, \ lbs/day}{Flow, \ MGD \times 8.34 \ lb/mg/L/MG} \qquad (2.11)$$

Example 2.32

Problem:

The disinfection process uses 4,820 lb/day of chlorine to disinfect a flow of 20 MGD. What is the concentration of chlorine applied to the effluent?

Solution:

$$\text{concentration} = \frac{4,820}{20\ \text{MGD} \times 8.34\ \text{lb/mg/L/MG}} = 29\ \text{mg/L}$$

2.12.1.10 Pounds to Flow in Million Gallons Per Day

$$\text{flow} = \frac{\text{quantity, lb/day}}{\text{concentration, mg/L} \times 8.34\ \text{lb/mg/L/MG}} \qquad (2.12)$$

Example 2.33

Problem:

You must remove 7,640 pounds of solids from the activated sludge process per day. The waste activated sludge concentration is 5,899 mg/L. How many million gallons per day of waste activated sludge must be removed?

Solution:

$$\text{flow} = \frac{7,640\ \text{lb}}{5,899\ \text{mg/L} \times 8.34\ \text{lb/mg/L/MG}} = 0.16\ \text{MGD}$$

2.12.1.11 Million Gal/Day (MGD) to Gallons/Minute (gpm)

$$\text{Flow} = \frac{\text{flow, MGD} \times 1,000,000\ \text{gal/MG}}{1,440\ \text{minutes/day}} \qquad (2.13)$$

Example 2.34

Problem:

The current flow rate is 4.50 MGD. What is the flow rate in gallons per minute?

$$\text{Flow} = \frac{4.50\ \text{MGD} \times 1,000,000\ \text{gal/MG}}{1,440\ \text{minutes/day}} = 3,125\ \text{gpm}$$

2.12.1.12 Million Gallons/Day (MGD) to Gallons/Day (gpd)

$$\text{flow} = \text{flow, MGD} \times 1,000,000\ \text{gal/MG} \qquad (2.14)$$

Example 2.35

Problem:

The influent meter reads 27.5 MGD. What is the current flow rate in gallons per day?

Solution:

$$\text{flow} = 27.5 \text{ MGD} \times 1{,}000{,}000 \text{ gal/MG} = 27{,}500{,}000 \text{ gpd}$$

2.12.1.13 Million Gal/Day (MGD) to Cubic Feet/Second (cfs)

$$\text{Flow, cfs} = \text{Flow, MGD} \times 1.55 \text{ cfs/MGD} \qquad (2.15)$$

Example 2.36

Problem:

The flow rate entering the grit channel is 2.19 MGD. What is the flow rate in cubic feet per second?

Solution:

$$\text{flow} = 2.19 \text{ MGD} \times 1.55 \text{ cfs/MGD} = 3.4 \text{ cfs}$$

2.12.1.14 Gallons/Minute (gpm) To Million Gallons/Day (MGD)

$$\text{flow, MGD} = \frac{\text{flow, gpm} \times 1{,}440 \text{ minutes/day}}{1{,}000{,}000 \text{ gallons/MG}} \qquad (2.16)$$

Example 2.37

Problem:

The flow meter indicates that the current flow rate is 1,440 gpm. What is the flow rate in MGD?

Solution:

$$\text{flow} = \frac{1{,}440 \text{ gpm} \times 1{,}440 \text{ minutes/day}}{1{,}000{,}000 \text{ gallons/MG}} = 2.0736 \text{ MGD}$$

✓ *Note*: unless a higher degree of accuracy is required, this number would be rounded off to 2 decimal places (2.07).

2.12.1.15 Gallons per day (gpd) to million gallons per day (MGD)

$$\text{flow, MGD} = \frac{\text{flow, MGD}}{1,000,000 \text{ gal/MG}} \qquad (2.17)$$

Example 2.38

Problem:

The totalizing flow meter indicates that 30,669,969 gallons of wastewater have entered the plant in the past 24 hours. What is the flow rate in MGD?

Solution:

$$\text{flow} = \frac{30,669,969 \text{ gal/day}}{1,000,000 \text{ gal/MG}} = 30.669969 \text{ MGD}$$

✓ *Note*: unless a higher degree of accuracy is required, this number would be rounded to 2 decimal places (30.67).

2.12.1.16 Flow in Cubic Feet/Second (cfs) to Million Gal/day (MGD)

$$\text{flow, MGD} = \frac{\text{flow, cfs}}{1.55 \text{ cfs/MG}} \qquad (2.18)$$

Example 2.39

Problem:

The flow in a channel is determined to be 3.76 cubic feet per second (cfs). What is the flow rate in million gallons per day (MGD)?

Solution:

$$\text{flow} = \frac{3.76 \text{ cfs}}{1.55 \text{ cfs/MG}} = 2.4258 \text{ MGD}$$

✓ *Note*: unless a higher degree of accuracy is required, this number would be rounded off to 2 decimal places (2.43 MGD).

2.12.1.17 Temperature Conversions

Most wastewater operators are familiar with the formulas used for Fahrenheit and Celsius temperature conversions:

$$°C = 5/9(°F - 32) \qquad\qquad (2.19)$$

$$°F = 9/5(°C) + 32 \qquad\qquad (2.20)$$

The difficulty arises when one is required to recall these formulas from memory.

✓ *Note*: Probably the easiest way to recall these important formulas is to remember three basic steps for both Fahrenheit and Celsius conversions:

(1) Add 40°
(2) Multiply by the appropriate fraction (5/9 or 9/5)
(3) Subtract 40°

Obviously, the only variable in this method is the choice of 5/9 or 9/5 in the multiplication step. To make the proper choice, you must be familiar with two scales. On the Fahrenheit scale the freezing point of water is 32°, whereas it is 0° on the Celsius scale. The boiling point of water is 212° on the Fahrenheit scale and 100° on the Celsius scale.

What does all this mean?

It means, for example, that at the same temperature, higher numbers are associated with the Fahrenheit scale and lower numbers with the Celsius scale. This is an important relationship that helps you decide whether to multiply by 5/9 or 9/5. Let's look at a few conversion problems to see how the three-step process works.

Example 2.40

Suppose that you wish to convert 240°F to Celsius. Using the three-step process we proceed as follows:

(1) *Step 1*: add 40°

$$\begin{array}{r} 240° \\ +40° \\ \hline 280° \end{array}$$

(2) *Step 2*: 280° must be multiplied by either 5/9 or 9/5. Since the conversion

is to the Celsius scale, you will be moving to a number *smaller* than 280. Through reason and observation it is obvious that if 280 is multiplied by 9/5, it would almost be the same as multiplying by 2, which would double 280 rather than make it smaller. On the other hand, if you multiply by 5/9 it is about the same as multiplying by 1/2, which would cut 280 in half. Since in this problem you wish to move to a smaller number, you should multiply by 5/9:

$$(5/9)(280°) = 156.0°C$$

(3) *Step 3*: Now subtract 40°

$$\begin{array}{r} 156.0°C \\ -40.0°C \\ \hline 116.0°C \end{array}$$

Therefore, 240°F = 116.0°C

Example 2.41

Convert 22°C to Fahrenheit

(1) *Step 1*: add 40°

$$\begin{array}{r} 22° \\ +40° \\ \hline 62° \end{array}$$

Since you are converting from Celsius to Fahrenheit, you are moving from a smaller to larger number, and 9/5 should be used in the multiplication:

(2) *Step 2*:

$$(9/5)(62°) = 112°$$

(3) *Step 3*: Subtract 40°

$$\begin{array}{r} 112° \\ -40° \\ \hline 72° \end{array}$$

Thus, 22°C = 72°F

Obviously, it is useful to know how to make these temperature conversion calculations. However, in practical in situ or non-in situ operations you may wish to use a temperature conversion table.

2.13 TABLE OF EQUIVALENTS, FORMULAE AND SYMBOLS

In addition to being able to perform mathematical unit conversions correctly, the wastewater operator must also be able to work with equivalents, formulae and mathematical symbols.

✓ *Note*: For licensure examinations, the examination center normally provides a formula sheet that usually includes equivalents and symbols used to aid in solving questions provided in the examination.

Because this made-easy guide is designed not only to be used in studying for licensure examinations but also for practical on-the-job applications, equivalents, formulae, and symbols are included, as a ready reference, in Table 2.2.

TABLE 2.2. Equivalents, Formulae, and Symbols.

Equivalents
12 inches = 1 foot
36 inches = 1 yard
144 inches^2 = 1 foot^2
9 feet^2 = 1 yard
43,560 feet^2 = 1 acre
1 foot^3 = 1,728 inch^3
1 foot^3 of water = 7.48 gallons
1 foot^3 of water weighs = 62.4 lbs
1 gallon of water weighs = 8.34 lbs
1 liter = 1,000 milliliters
1 gram = 1,000 milligrams
1 million gal/day = 694 gal/min
= 1.547 ft^3/sec
Average BOD/capita/day = 0.17 lbs*
Average SS/capita/day = 0.20*
Average daily flow = assume 100 gal/capita/dy*

*These values are for residential wastewater, industrial wastewater may be significantly different.

(continued)

TABLE 2.2 (continued). Equivalents, Formulae, and Symbols.

Symbols
A = Area
V = Velocity
t = time
SVI = Sludge Volume Index
Vol = Volume
# = pounds (lbs)
eff = effluent
W = width
D = depth
L = length
Q = flow
r = radius
π = pi (3.14)
WAS = Waste Activated Sludge
RAS = Return Activated Sludge
MLSS = Mixed Liquor Suspended Solids
MLVSS = Mixed Liquor Volatile Suspended Solids

Formulae

$$SVI = \frac{volume}{concentration} \times 100$$

$$Q = A \times V$$

$$Detention\ Time = \frac{volume}{Q}$$

$$Volume = L \times W \times D$$

$$Area = W \times L$$

$$Circular\ Area = \pi \times D^2 (= 0.785 \times D^2)$$

$$Circumference = \pi D$$

$$Hydraulic\ Loading\ Rate = \frac{Q}{A}$$

$$Sludge\ Age = \frac{\#MLSS\ in\ Aeration\ Tank}{\#SS\ in\ Primary\ Eff/day}$$

$$MRCT = \frac{\#\ SS\ in\ Secondary\ System\ (aeration\ tank + sec.\ clarifier)}{\#\ WAS/day + \#SS\ in\ Eff/day}$$

$$Organic\ Loading\ Rate = \frac{\#\ BOD/day}{Volume}$$

2.14 PRACTICAL WASTEWATER TREATMENT MATH OPERATIONS

2.14.1 VOLUME CALCULATIONS

Performing *volume* calculations goes hand-in-hand with wastewater operations. All one need do is to look around his or her plant site to understand why this is the case. In just about any direction you look, you will see tanks, channels, pipelines, pits, trenches, and/or ponds. Many of these vessels and structures are important parts of various treatment unit processes, and calculating their volumes is sometimes required.

✓ *Note*: For many calculations, the volumes are expressed in gallons. To convert from cubic feet to gallons volume, a factor of 7.48 gal/cu ft is used. Refer to Section 2.12 for a more detailed discussion of conversions.

The general equation for most volume calculations is

$$\text{Volume} = \text{Area} \times \text{Depth or Height} \tag{2.21}$$

2.14.1.1 Tank Volume Calculation

Rectangular or cylindrically shaped tanks are typically used in wastewater treatment unit processes (see Figure 2.3). The equation for volume calculations (rectangular tanks) is

$$V = (lw)(d) \tag{2.22}$$

Figure 2.4 shows a cylindrical tank. The equation for volume calculation in circular or cylindrical tanks is:

$$V = (0.785)(D^2)(d) \tag{2.23}$$

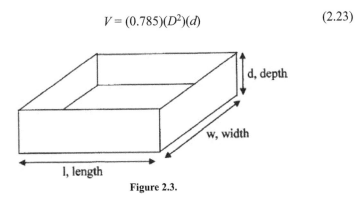

Figure 2.3.

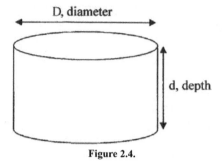

Figure 2.4.

Let's take a look at a couple of tank volume calculations.

Example 2.42

Tank volume (rectangular)

Problem:

Calculate the volume of the rectangular tank shown in Figure 2.5 in cubic feet.

✓ *Note*: If a drawing is not supplied with the problem, draw a rough picture or diagram. Make sure you label or identify the parts of the diagram from the information given in the question.

Solution:

$$\begin{aligned}
\text{volume, cu ft} &= (lw)(d)\\
&= (50 \text{ ft})(12 \text{ ft})(8 \text{ ft})\\
&= 4{,}800 \text{ cu ft}
\end{aligned}$$

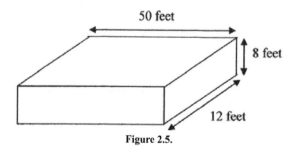

Figure 2.5.

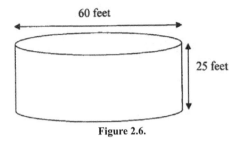

60 feet

25 feet

Figure 2.6.

Example 2.43

Tank volume (Circular)

Problem:

The diameter of a tank is 60 ft. When the water depth is 25 ft, what is the volume of wastewater in the tank, in gallons?

✓ *Note*: Draw a diagram similar to that shown in Figure 2.6.

Solution:

$$\text{volume, gal} = (0.785)(D^2)(d)(7.48 \text{ gal/cu ft})$$

✓ *Note*: Remember, the solution requires the result in gallons; thus, we must include 7.48 gal/cu ft in the operation to ensure the result is in gallons.

$$= (0.785)(60 \text{ ft})(60 \text{ ft})(25 \text{ ft})(7.48 \text{ gal/cu ft})$$
$$= 528{,}462 \text{ gal}$$

Now let's take a look at another cylindrical or circular tank problem, one with a different twist, so to speak.

Example 2.44

Problem:

A cylindrical tank is 10 ft in diameter and 20 ft in height. What is the approximate capacity in liters?

✓ *Note*: Don't forget to draw a rough diagram of the tank and dimensions.

Solution:

Calculate the tank volume using the following formula:

$$\text{Tank Volume} = \frac{\pi D^2}{4} \times H$$

$$= \frac{\pi(10 \text{ ft})^2}{4}(20 \text{ ft}) \qquad (2.24)$$

$$= 1{,}571 \text{ cu ft}$$

✓ *Note*: Remember, the problem asked for the tank capacity in "liters".

Convert 1,571 cu ft to liters:

$$= 1{,}571 \times 7.48 \text{ gal/cu ft} \times 3.785 \text{ L/gal}$$
$$= 44{,}472 \text{ L}$$

2.14.1.2 Channel Volume Calculations

Channels are commonly used in wastewater treatment (e.g., contact tanks, etc.). Channels are typically rectangular-or trapezoidal-shaped. For rectangular channels, use Equation 2.23.

$$V = (lw)(d)$$

Example 2.45

Channel Volume (rectangular)

Problem:

Determine the volume of wastewater (in cu ft) in the section of rectangular channel shown in Figure 2.7 when the wastewater is 5 ft deep.

Solution:

$$\text{volume, cu ft} = (lw)(d)$$
$$= (600 \text{ ft})(6 \text{ ft})(5 \text{ ft})$$
$$= 18{,}000 \text{ cu ft}$$

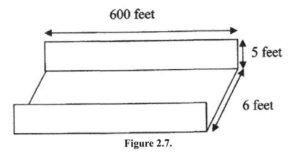

600 feet

5 feet

6 feet

Figure 2.7.

Example 2.46

Channel Volume (trapezoidal)

$$\text{Volume, cu ft} = \frac{(b_1 + b_2)}{2}(d)(l) \tag{2.25}$$

Problem:

Determine the volume of wastewater (in gallons) in the section of trapezoidal channel when the wastewater depth is 5 ft.

Solution:

Given: $b_1 = 4'$ across the bottom
$b_2 = 10'$ across water surface
$l = 1,000'$

$$\text{volume, gal} = \frac{(b_1 + b_2)}{2}(d)(l)(7.48 \text{ gal/cu ft})$$

$$= \frac{(4 \text{ ft} + 10 \text{ ft})}{2}(5 \text{ ft})(1000 \text{ ft})(7.48 \text{ gal/cu ft})$$

$$= (7)(5)(1000)(7.48)$$

$$= 261,800 \text{ gal}$$

2.14.1.3 Volume of Circular Pipeline

$$\text{volume, cu ft} = (0.0785)(D^2)(l) \tag{2.26}$$

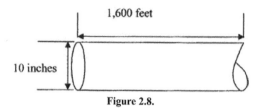

Figure 2.8.

Example 2.47

Circular Pipe Volume

Problem:

What is the capacity in gallons of wastewater of a 10-inch diameter, 1,600 ft section of pipeline (see Figure 2.8)?

Convert 10 in to feet (12 in/10 in = 0.833 ft)

Solution:

$$\text{volume, gal} = (0.785)(D^2)(l)(7.48\text{gal/cu ft})$$
$$= (0.785)(0.833)(0.833)(1{,}600 \text{ ft})(7.48 \text{ gal/cu ft})$$
$$= 6{,}519 \text{ gal}$$

Example 2.48

Problem:

Approximately how many gallons of wastewater would 600 ft of 8-in pipe hold?

Solution:

$$\text{Volume} = \frac{\pi(D^2)}{4}(L)$$
$$= \frac{\pi(0.67 \text{ ft})^2}{4}(600 \text{ ft})$$
$$= 212 \text{ cu ft}$$

Convert: 212 cu ft to gallons

$$= 212 \text{ cu ft} \times 7.48 \text{ gal/cu ft}$$
$$= 1,586 \text{ gallons}$$

2.14.1.4 Pit or Trench Volumes

Pits and trenches are often used in wastewater treatment plant operations for various unit processes. Thus, it is important to be able to determine their volumes. The calculations used in determining pit or trench volumes are similar to tank and channel volume calculations, with one difference—the volume is often expressed as cubic yards rather than cubic feet or gallons.

In calculating cubic yards, typically two approaches are used:

(1) Calculate the cubic feet volume, then convert to cubic volume.

$$\text{cu yards} = \frac{(\text{cu ft})}{27 \text{ cu ft/yd}} \qquad (2.27)$$

(2) Express all dimensions in yards so that the resulting volume calculated will be cubic yards.

$$(\text{yds})(\text{yds})(\text{yds}) = \text{cu yds} \qquad (2.28)$$

Example 2.49

Problem:

A trench is to be excavated 3 feet wide, 5 feet deep, and 800 feet long. What is the cubic yards volume of the trench?

✓ *Note*: Remember, draw a diagram similar to the one shown in Figure 2.9.

Solution:

$$\text{Volume, cu ft} = (lw)(d)$$
$$= (800 \text{ ft})(3 \text{ ft})(5 \text{ ft})$$
$$= 12,000 \text{ cu ft}$$

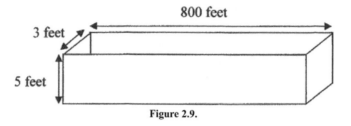

Figure 2.9.

Now convert cu ft volume to cu yds:

$$= \frac{12,000 \text{ cu ft}}{27 \text{ cu ft/cu yds}}$$
$$= 444 \text{ cu yds}$$

Now let's take a look at an example where we express all dimensions in yards so we can calculate the volume in cubic yards.

Example 2.50

Problem:

What is the cubic yard volume of a trench 600 ft long, 2.5 ft wide, and 4 ft deep?

Solution:

The first thing you must do is to convert dimensions in feet to yards before beginning the volume calculation:

$$\text{Length} = \frac{600 \text{ ft}}{3 \text{ ft/yd}} = 200 \text{ yds}$$

$$\text{Width} = \frac{2.5 \text{ ft}}{3 \text{ ft/yd}} = 0.83 \text{ yds}$$

$$\text{Depth} = \frac{5 \text{ft}}{3 \text{ ft/yd}} = 1.67 \text{ yds}$$

Now make a diagram and label dimensions as shown in Figure 2.10.

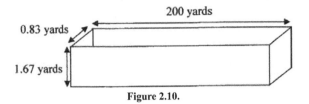

Figure 2.10.

volume, cu yds = $(lw)(d)$

$\quad\quad = (200 \text{ yds})(0.83 \text{ yds})(1.67 \text{ yds})$

$\quad\quad = 277$ cu yds

2.14.1.5 Pond Volumes

Ponds and/or oxidation ditches are commonly used in wastewater treatment operations. To determine the volume of a pond (or ditch), it is necessary to determine if all four sides slope or if just two sides slope. This is important because the means used to determine volume will vary depending on the number of sloping sides.

If only two of the sides slope and the ends are vertical, we calculate the volume using the equation:

$$V = \frac{(b_1 + b_2)}{2}(d)(l) \quad\quad\quad (2.29)$$

However, when all sides slope as shown in Figure 2.11, the equation we use must include average length and average width dimensions. Use the equation:

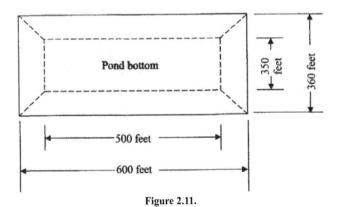

Figure 2.11.

$$V = \frac{(l_1 + l_2)}{2} \frac{(w_1 + w_2)}{2}(\text{depth}) \qquad (2.30)$$

Let's take a look at an example problem for determining the slope of a pond where all sides slope.

Example 2.51

Problem:

A pond is 6 ft deep with side slopes of 2:1 (2 ft horizontal: 1 ft vertical). Using the data supplied in Figure 2.11, calculate the volume of the pond in cubic feet.

Solution:

$$V = \frac{(l_1 + l_2)}{2} \frac{(w_1 + w_2)}{2}(\text{depth})$$

$$= \frac{(500 \text{ ft} + 600 \text{ ft})}{2} \frac{(350 \text{ ft} + 360 \text{ ft})}{2}(6 \text{ ft})$$

$$= (550 \text{ ft})(355 \text{ ft})(6 \text{ ft})$$

$$= 1,171,500 \text{ cu ft}$$

2.14.1.6 Flow Calculations

In wastewater treatment, one of the major concerns of the operator is not only to maintain flow, but also to measure it. Normally, flow measurements are determined by metering devices. These devices measure wastewater flow at a particular moment (instantaneous flow) or over a specified time period (total flow). Instantaneous flow can also be determined mathematically. In this section, we discuss how to mathematically determine instantaneous and average flow rates and also how to make flow conversions.

2.14.1.6.1 Instantaneous Flow Rates

In determining instantaneous flows rates through channels, tanks, and pipelines, we can use the $Q = AV$ equation.

✓ *Note*: It is important to remember that when using an equation such as $Q = AV$, the units on the left side of the equation must match those units on the right side of the equation (A and V) with respect to *volume* (cubic feet or gallons) and *time* (seconds, minutes, hours, or days).

Let's take a look at an example problem where we determine instantaneous flow rate (flow rate for any particular moment) by using the $Q = AV$ equation.

Example 2.52

Problem:

A channel 5 ft wide has water flowing to a depth of 2 ft. If the velocity through the channel is 2 feet per second (fps), what is the cubic feet per second (cfs) flow rate through the channel?

Solution:

$$Q, \text{cfs} = (A)(V, \text{fps})$$
$$= (5 \text{ ft})(2 \text{ ft})(2 \text{ fps})$$
$$= 20 \text{ cfs}$$

2.14.1.6.2 Instantaneous Flow Into and Out of a Rectangular Tank

One of the primary flow measurements the wastewater operator is commonly required to calculate is the flow through a tank. This measurement can be determined using the $Q = AV$ equation. For example, if the discharge valve to a tank were closed, the water level would begin to rise. If you time how fast the water rises, this would give you an indication of the velocity of flow into the tank. This information can be "plugged" into the $Q = VA$ equation to determine the flow rate through the tank. Let's take a look at an example.

Example 2.53

Problem:

A tank is 8 ft wide and 10 ft long. With the discharge valve closed, the influent to the tank causes the water level to rise 1.5 feet in one minute. What is the gpm flow into the tank?

Solution:

First, calculate the cfm flow rate:

$$Q, \text{cfm} = (A)(V, \text{fpm})$$
$$= (8 \text{ ft})(10 \text{ ft})(1.5 \text{ fpm})$$
$$= 120 \text{ cfm}$$

Then convert cfm flow rate to gpm flow rate:

$$(120 \text{ cfm})(7.48 \text{ gal/cu ft}) = 898 \text{ gpm}$$

How do we compute flow rate from a tank when the influent valve is closed and the discharge pump remains on, lowering the wastewater level in the tank?

Quite simply, actually. All one need do is time the rate of this drop in wastewater level so that the velocity of flow from the tank can be calculated. Then, we use the $Q = AV$ equation to determine the flow rate out of the tank, as illustrated in Example 2.54.

Example 2.54

Problem:

A tank is 8 ft wide and 10 ft long. The influent valve to the tank is closed and the water level drops 2.5 ft in 2 minutes. What is the gpm flow from the tank?

$$\text{drop rate} = 2.5 \text{ ft/2 mi}$$

$$= 1.25 \text{ ft/min}$$

First, calculate the cfm flow rate:

$$Q, \text{cfm} = (A)(V, \text{fpm})$$

$$= (8 \text{ ft})(10 \text{ ft})(1.25 \text{ fpm})$$

$$= 100 \text{ cfm}$$

Then, convert cfm flow rate to gpm flow rate:

$$(100 \text{ cfm})(7.48 \text{ gal/cu ft}) = 748 \text{ gpm}$$

2.14.1.6.3 Flow Rate Into a Cylindrical Tank

We can use the same basic method to determine the flow rate when the tank is cylindrical in shape, as illustrated in Example 2.55.

Example 2.55

Problem:

The discharge valve to a 25-ft diameter cylindrical tank is closed. If the water rises at a rate of 12 inches in four minutes, what is the gpm flow into the tank?

Solution:

$$\text{Rise} = 12 \text{ in.}/4 \text{ min}$$

$$= 1 \text{ ft}/4 \text{ min}$$

$$= 0.25 \text{ ft/min}$$

First, calculate the cfm flow into the tank:

$$Q, \text{cfm} = (A)(V, \text{fpm})$$

$$= (0.785)(25 \text{ ft})(25 \text{ ft})(0.25 \text{ ft/min})$$

$$= 123 \text{ cfm}$$

Then, convert cfm flow rate to gpm flow rate:

$$(123 \text{ cfm})(7.48 \text{ gal/cu ft}) = 920 \text{ gpm}$$

2.14.1.6.4 Flow Through a Full Pipeline

The flow through a pipeline is of considerable interest to wastewater collections workers and to operators. The flow rate can be calculated using the $Q = AV$ equation. The cross-sectional area of a round pipe is a circle, so the area, A, is represented by $(0.785)(D^2)$.

✓ *Note*: To avoid errors in terms, it is prudent to express pipe diameters as feet.

Example 2.56

Problem:

The flow through an 8-inch diameter pipeline is moving at a velocity of 3 ft/sec. What is the cfs flow rate through the full pipeline?
Convert 8 in. to feet:

$$8 \text{ in.}/12 \text{ in.} = 0.67 \text{ ft}$$

$$Q, \text{cfs} = (A)(V, \text{fps})$$

$$= (0.785)(0.67 \text{ ft})(0.67 \text{ ft})(3 \text{ fps})$$

$$= 1.1 \text{ cfs}$$

2.14.1.7 Velocity Calculations

To determine the velocity of flow in a channel or pipeline, we use the $Q = AV$ equation. However, to use the equation correctly, we must transpose the equation. We simply write into the equation the information given and then transpose for the unknown (V in this case), as illustrated in Example 2.56 for channels and 2.57 for pipelines.

Example 2.57

Problem:

A channel has a rectangular cross-section. The channel is 6 ft wide with wastewater flowing to a depth of 2 ft. If the flow rate through the channel is 8,500 gpm, what is the velocity of the wastewater in the channel (ft/sec)?
Convert gpm to cfs:

$$\frac{8,500 \text{ gpm}}{(7.48 \text{ gal})(60 \text{ sec})} = 18.9 \text{ cfs}$$

$$Q, \text{cfs} = (A)(V, \text{fps})$$

$$18.9 \text{ cfs} = (6 \text{ ft})(2 \text{ ft})(\text{unknown, fps})$$

$$\text{Velocity (the unknown, fps)} = \frac{18.9}{(6)(2)}$$

$$V = 1.58 \text{ fps}$$

Example 2.58

Problem:

A full 8-inch diameter pipe delivers 250 gpm. What is the velocity of flow in the pipeline (ft/sec)?
Convert:

$$8 \text{ in.}/12 \text{ in. to feet} = 0.67 \text{ ft}$$

Convert: gpm to cfs flow:

$$\frac{250 \text{ gpm}}{(7.48 \text{gal/cuft})(60 \text{sec/min})} = 0.56 \text{ cfs}$$

$$0.56 \text{ cfs} = (0.785)(0.67 \text{ ft})(0.67 \text{ ft})(\text{unknown}, V, \text{fps})$$

$$V = \frac{0.56 \text{ cfs}}{(0.785)(0.67)(0.67)}$$

$$V = 1.6 \text{ fps}$$

2.14.1.8 Average Flow Rates Calculations

Flow rates in a wastewater treatment system vary considerably during the course of a day, week, month, or year. Therefore, when computing flow rates for trend analysis or for other purposes, an average flow rate is used to determine the typical flow rate. Example 2.59 illustrates one way to calculate an average flow rate.

Example 2.59

Problem:

The following flows were recorded for the week:

Monday	8.2 MGD
Tuesday	8.0 MGD
Wednesday	7.3 MGD
Thursday	7.6 MGD
Friday	8.2 MGD
Saturday	8.9 MGD
Sunday	7.7 MGD

What was the average daily flow rate for the week?

$$\text{Average Daily Flow} = \frac{\text{Total of all Sample Flows}}{\text{Number of Days}}$$

$$= \frac{55.9 \text{ MGD}}{7 \text{Days}} \qquad (2.31)$$

$$= 8.0 \text{ MGD}$$

2.14.1.9 Flow Conversion Calculations

One of the tasks involving calculations that the wastewater operator is typically called on to perform involves converting one expression of flow to another.

The ability to do this is also a necessity for those preparing for licensure examinations.

Probably the easiest way to accomplish flow conversions is to employ the box method illustrated in Figure 2.12.

When using the box method, it is important to remember that moving from a smaller box to a larger box requires multiplication by the factor indicated. Moving from a larger box to a smaller box requires division by the factor indicated.

From Figure 2.12, it should be obvious that memorizing the 9 boxes and the units in each box is not that difficult. The values of 60, 1440, 7.48 and 8.34 are not that difficult to remember either—it is a matter of remembering the exact placement of the units and the values that is key to memorizing the box. Once this is accomplished, you have obtained a powerful tool that will enable you to make flow conversions in a relatively easy manner.

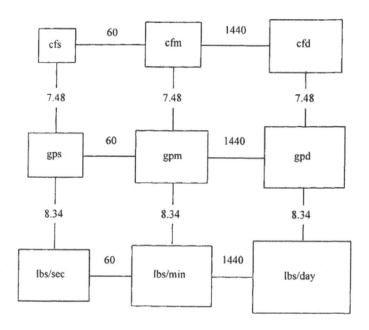

cfs = cubic feet per second
cfm = cubic feet per minute
cfd = cubic feet per day

gps = gallons per second
gpm = gallons per minute
gpd = gallons per day

*The factors shown in the diagram have the following units associated with them: 60 sec/min, 1440 min/day, 7.48 gal/cu ft, and 8.34 lbs/gal.

Figure 2.12. Flow conversions using the box method.

2.14.1.10 Chemical Dosage Calculations (Chlorine/Hypochlorite)

Chemicals are used extensively in wastewater treatment plant operations. Wastewater treatment plant operators add chemicals to various unit processes for slime-growth control, corrosion control, odor control, grease removal, BOD reduction, pH control, sludge-bulking control, ammonia oxidation, bacterial reduction, and for other reasons.

In order to apply any chemical dose correctly, it is important to be able to make certain dosage calculations. One of the most frequently used calculations in wastewater mathematics is the conversion of milligrams per liter (mg/L) concentration to pounds per day (lbs/day) or pounds (lbs) dosage or loading. The general types of mg/L to lbs/day or lbs calculations are for chemical dosage, BOD, COD, or SS loading/removal, pounds of solids under aeration and WAS pumping rate. These calculations are usually made using either of the following Equations (2.32) or (2.33):

$$(\text{mg/L})(\text{MGD flow})(8.34 \text{ lbs/gal}) = \text{lb/day} \qquad (2.32)$$

$$(\text{mg/L})(\text{MG volume})(8.34 \text{ lbs/gal}) = \text{lb} \qquad (2.33)$$

✓ *Note*: If mg/L concentration represents a concentration in a flow, then million gallons per day (MGD) flow is used as the second factor. However, if the concentration pertains to a tank or pipeline volume, then million gallons (MG) volume is used as the second factor.

2.14.1.10.1 Chlorine Dosage

Chlorine is a powerful oxidizer that is commonly used in wastewater treatment for disinfection, odor control, bulking control, and other applications. When chlorine is added to a unit process, we want to ensure that the amount to be added is calculated and measured accurately.

In describing the amount of chemical added or required, two ways are used:

- milligrams per liter (mg/L)
- pounds per day (lb/day)

In the conversion from mg/L (or ppm) concentration to lb/day, we use equation 2.34.

$$(\text{mg/L})(\text{MGD})(8.34) = \text{lbs/day} \qquad (2.34)$$

✓ *Note*: In previous years, it was normal practice to use the expression parts per million (ppm) as an expression of concentration, since 1 mg/L = 1 ppm. However, current practice is to use mg/L as the preferred expression of concentration.

Example 2.60

Problem:

Determine the chlorinator setting (lbs/day) needed to treat a flow of 8 MGD with a chlorine dose of 4 mg/L.

Solution:

$$(mg/L)(MGD)(8.34) = lb/day$$
$$(4\ mg/L)(8\ MGD)(8.34\ lb/gal) = lb/day$$
$$= 267\ lb/day$$

Example 2.61

Problem:

What should the chlorinator setting be (lbs/day) to treat a flow of 3 MGD if the chlorine demand is 12 mg/L and a chlorine residual of 2 mg/L is desired?

✓ *Note*: The chlorine demand is the amount of chlorine used in reacting with various components of the wastewater, such as harmful organisms and other organic and inorganic substances. When the chlorine demand has been satisfied, these reactions stop.

$$(mg/L)(MGD)(8.34) = lb/day$$

✓ *Note*: In order to find the unknown value (lb/day), we must first determine chlorine dose. To do this, we must use equation 2.36.

$$chl.\ dose,\ mg/L = chl.\ demand,\ mg/L + chl.\ residual,\ mg/L$$
$$= 12\ mg/L + 2\ mg/L \qquad (2.35)$$
$$= 14\ mg/L$$

Then, we can make the mg/L to lbs/day calculation:

$$(14\ mg/L)(3\ MGD\ flow)(8.34\ lbs/gal) = 300\ lb/day$$

2.14.1.10.2 Hypochlorite Dosage

At many wastewater facilities, sodium hypochlorite or calcium hypochlorite is used instead of chlorine. The reasons for substituting hypochlorite for chlorine vary. However, with the passage of stricter hazardous chemicals regulations under OSHA and the USEPA, many facilities are deciding to substitute the hazardous chemical chlorine with non-hazardous hypochlorite. Obviously, the potential liability involved with using deadly chlorine is also a factor involved in the decision to replace it with a less toxic chemical substance.

For whatever reason the wastewater treatment plant decides to substitute chlorine for hypochlorite, there are differences between the two chemicals, of which the wastewater operator needs to be aware. Let's look at chlorine first.

Chlorine is a hazardous material. Chlorine gas is used in wastewater treatment applications at 100% available chlorine. This is an important consideration to keep in mind when making or setting chlorine feed rates. For example, if the chlorine demand and residual requires 100 lbs/day chlorine, the chlorinator setting would be just that—100 lbs/24 hrs.

Hypochlorite is less hazardous than chlorine; it is similar to a strong bleach and comes in two forms: dry calcium hypochlorite (often referred to as HTH) and liquid sodium hypochlorite. Calcium hypochlorite contains about 65% available chlorine; sodium hypochlorite contains about 12–15% available chlorine (in industrial strengths).

✓ *Note*: Because either type of hypochlorite is not 100% pure chlorine, more lb/day must be fed into the system to obtain the same amount of chlorine for disinfection. This is an important economical consideration for those facilities thinking about substituting hypochlorite for chlorine. Some studies indicate that such a switch can increase operating costs, overall, by up to 3 times the cost of using chlorine.[7]

To calculate the lbs/day hypochlorite required, a two-step calculation is required:

Step 1:

$$mg/L(MGD(8.34)) = lbs/day$$

---

[7]Spellman, F. R., *Spellman's Standard Handbook for Wastewater Operators: Volume II Intermediate Level.* Lancaster, PA: Technomic Publishing Company, p. 40, 1999.

Step 2:

$$\frac{\text{Chlorine, lb/day}}{\text{\% Available}} \times 100 = \text{Hypochlorite, lb/day}$$

Example 2.62

Problem:

A total chlorine dosage of 10 mg/L is required to treat a particular wastewater. If the flow is 1.6 MGD and the hypochlorite has 65% available chlorine, how many lbs/day of hypochlorite will be required?

Solution:

Step 1: Calculate the lb/day chlorine required using the mg/L to lb/day equation:

$$(\text{mg/L})(\text{MGD})(8.34) = \text{lb/day}$$

$$(10 \text{ mg/L})(1.6 \text{ MGD})(8.34 \text{ lbs/gal}) = 133 \text{ lb/day}$$

Step 2: Calculate the lb/day hypochlorite required. Since only 65% of the hypochlorite is chlorine, more than 133 lb/day will be required:

$$\frac{133 \text{ lb/day Chlorine}}{65 \text{ Avail. Chlorine}} \times 100 = 205 \text{ lb/day hypochlorite}$$

Example 2.63

Problem:

A wastewater flow of 840,000 gpd requires a chlorine dose of 20 mg/L. If sodium hypochlorite (15% available chlorine) is to be used, how many lb/day of sodium hypochlorite are required? How many gal/day of sodium hypochlorite is this?

Solution:

Step 1: Calculate the lbs/day chlorine required:

$$(mg/L)(MGD)(8.34) = lb/day$$

$$(20\ mg/L)(0.84\ MGD)(8.34\ lbs/gal) = 140\ lb/day\ Chlorine$$

Step 2: Calculate the lb/day sodium hypochlorite solution:

$$\frac{140\ lb/day\ chlorine}{15\ avail.\ chlorine} \times 100 = 933\ lb/day\ hypochlorite$$

Step 3: Calculate the gal/day sodium hypochlorite:

$$\frac{933\ lb/day}{8.34\ lb/gal} = 112\ gal/day\ sodium\ hypochlorite$$

Now, let's look at a chlorine dosage-type problem from a slightly different view—the type of dosage problem that is typically encountered in wastewater operations.

Example 2.64

Problem:

How many pounds of chlorine gas are necessary for 5,000,000 gallons of wastewater at a dosage of 2 mg/L?

Solution:

Step 1: Calculate the pounds of chlorine required.

$$V,\ 10^6\ gal \times chlorine\ concentration\ (mg/L) \times 8.34 = lb\ chlorine$$

Step 2: Substitute $5 \times 10^6\ gal \times 2\ mg/L \times 8.34 = 83\ lb\ chlorine$

2.14.1.11 Other Chemical Additions

In addition to chlorinating and/or dechlorinating, another important function of wastewater operators is to make other chemical additions to unit processes. In this section we show how to calculate required amounts of chemicals (active ingredient), dry chemical feed rate, and liquid chemical feed rate.

2.14.1.11.1 Required Amount of Chemical (Active Ingredient)

$$(Active\ Ingredient)\ Chemical,\ lb/day =$$
$$Required\ Dose,\ mg/L \times Flow,\ MGD \times 8.34\ lb/mg/L/MG \qquad (2.36)$$

Example 2.65

Problem:

The laboratory jar test indicates a dose of 4.1 mg/L of ferric chloride is required. The flow rate is 5.65 MGD. How many pounds of ferric chloride will be required each day?

Solution:

$$Required\ (Active\ Ingredients)\ Amount,\ lbs/day$$
$$= 4.1\ mg/L \times 5.65\ MGD \times 8.34\ lbs/mg/L/MG$$
$$= 193.2\ lb/day$$

2.14.1.11.2 Required Amount of Chemical

Since industrial strength chemicals are normally less than 100% active ingredient, the amount of chemical must be adjusted to compensate for the inactive components.

$$Required\ Amount,\ lbs/day = \frac{Active\ Ingredient\ Required,\ lbs/day}{\%\ Active\ Ingredient} \qquad (2.37)$$

Example 2.66

Problem:

To achieve the desired phosphorus removal 200 pounds of ferric chloride must be added to daily flow. The feed solution is 66% ferric chloride. How many pounds of feed solution will be needed?

Solution:

$$Required\ Amount,\ lbs/day = \frac{200\ lbs/day}{0.66} = 303\ lbs/day$$

2.14.1.11.3 Dry Chemical Feed Rate

When a chemical is to be added in dry (powder, granular, etc.) form, the chemical feed rate can be expressed in units such as pounds per hour or grams per minute.

$$\text{Feed Rate, pounds/hour} = \frac{\text{Required Amount, lbs/day}}{24 \text{ hour/day}} \qquad (2.38)$$

$$\text{Feed Rate, grams/minute} = \frac{\text{Required Amount, lbs/day} \times 454 \text{ g/lb}}{1{,}440 \text{ min/day}} \qquad (2.39)$$

Example 2.67

Problem:

The plant must feed 275 pounds per day of high test hypochlorite (HTH) powder chlorine to reduce odors. What is the required feed rate in: (a) pounds per hour and (b) grams per minute?

Solution:

$$\text{(a) Feed Rate, lbs/hr} = \frac{275 \text{ lbs/day}}{24 \text{ hours/day}} = 11.5 \text{ lbs/hour}$$

$$\text{(b) Feed Rate, grams/minute} = \frac{275 \text{ lbs/day} \times 454 \text{ g/lb}}{1{,}440 \text{ minutes/day}} = 87 \text{ g/min}$$

2.14.1.11.4 Liquid Chemical Feed Rate

If you feed a chemical in its liquid form, the required amount (pounds, grams, etc.) of process chemical must be converted to an equivalent volume (gallons, milliliters, etc.). This volume is then converted to the measurement system of the solution feeder (gallons/day, milliliters/minute, etc.).

✓ *Note*: You may find the weight of a gallon of the process chemical printed on the container label or the material safety data sheet (MSDS). Or you may also determine weight per gallon, if the specific gravity of the chemical is supplied, using the procedure described in Section 2.14.1.17.

$$\text{Feed Rate, gpd} = \frac{\text{Required Amount of Chemical, lbs/day}}{\text{Weight per Gallon, lbs/gal}} \qquad (2.40)$$

$$\text{Feed Rate, Ml/min} = \frac{\text{Required Amount, lbs/day} \times 3{,}785 \text{ Ml/gal}}{\text{Weight per Gallon} \times 1{,}440 \text{ min/day}} \qquad (2.41)$$

$$\text{Feed Rate, Ml/min} = \frac{\text{Required Amount, lbs/day} \times 3{,}785 \text{ Ml/gal}}{\text{Weight per Gallon} \times 1{,}440 \text{ min/day}} \qquad (2.42)$$

Example 2.68

Problem:

To achieve phosphorus removal the plant must add 812 lbs of ferric chloride feed solution each day. The ferric chloride solution weights 11.1 lbs/gallon. What is the required feed rate (a) in gallons per day; (b) gallons per minute; and (c) milliliters per minute?

Solution:

$$\text{(a) Feed Rate, gpd} = \frac{812 \text{ lbs/day}}{11.1 \text{ lbs/gal}} = 73 \text{gpd}$$

$$\text{(b) Feed Rate, gpm} = \frac{812 \text{ lbs/day}}{11.1 \text{ lbs/gal} \times 1{,}440 \text{ min/day}} = 0.05 \text{ gpm}$$

$$\text{(c) Feed Rate Ml/min} = \frac{812 \text{ lbs/day} \times 3{,}785 \text{ Mi/gal}}{11.1 \text{ lbs/gal} \times 1{,}440 \text{ min/day}} = 192 \text{ Ml/min}$$

2.14.1.12 Practical Percentage Calculations

The words "per cent" mean "by the hundred." Percentage is often designated by the symbol %. Thus, 10% means 10 percent or 10/100 or 0.10. These equivalents may be written in the reverse order: 0.10 = 10/100 = 10%. In wastewater treatment, percent is frequently used to express plant performance and for control of sludge treatment processes.

✓ *Note*: To determine percent, divide the quantity you wish to express as a percent by the total quantity, and then multiply by 100.

$$\text{percent} = \frac{\text{quantity} \times 100}{\text{total}} \qquad (2.43)$$

Let's look at a couple of percent problems typically performed in wastewater treatment operations.

Example 2.69

Problem:

The plant operator removes 16,000 gallons of sludge from the settling tank. The sludge contains 1,320 gallons of solids. What is the percent solids in the sludge?

Solution:

$$\text{Percent} = \frac{1,320 \text{ gal}}{16,000 \text{ gal}} \times 100$$

$$= 8.25\%$$

Example 2.70

Problem:

Sludge contains 5.3% solids. What is the concentration of solids in decimal percent? (A decimal percent is a percentage expressed in decimal form.)

Solution:

$$\text{decimal percent} = \frac{5.3\%}{100} = 0.053$$

✓ *Note*: To determine what quantity a percent equals, first convert the percent to a decimal; then, multiply by the total quantity.

$$\text{quantity} = \text{total} \times \text{decimal percent} \qquad (2.44)$$

Example 2.71

Problem:

Sludge drawn from the settling tank is 8% solids. If 2,600 gallons of sludge are withdrawn, how many gallons of solids are removed?

Solution:

$$\text{gallons} = \frac{8\%}{100} \times 2{,}600 \text{ gallons}$$
$$= 208 \text{ gallons}$$

2.14.1.13 Arithmetic Average (or Arithmetic Mean)

During the day-to-day operation of a wastewater treatment plant, much data must be collected. The data, if properly evaluated, can provide useful information for trend analysis and can indicate how well the plant or unit process is operating. However, because there may be much variation in the data information, it is often difficult to determine trends in performance.

Arithmetic average, as we have seen above in Section 2.9, refers to a statistical calculation used to describe a series of numbers, such as test results. By being expressed as an *average*, a group of data is represented by a single number. This number may be considered typical of the group. The *arithmetic mean* is the most commonly used measurement of average value.

✓ *Note*: When evaluating information based on averages, remember that the "average" reflects the general nature of the group and does not necessarily reflect any one element of that group.

Arithmetic average is calculated by dividing the sum of all of the available data points (test results) by the number of test results.

$$\frac{\text{Test } 1 + \text{Test } 2 + \text{Test } 3 + \ldots + \text{Test } N}{\text{Number of Tests Performed } (N)} \tag{2.45}$$

Let's take a look at a couple of examples of how average is determined.

Example 2.72

Problem:

Effluent BOD test results for the treatment plant during the month of September are shown below.

Test 1	22 mg/L
Test 2	30 mg/L
Test 3	24 mg/L
Test 4	15 mg/L

What is the average effluent BOD for the month of September?

Solution:

$$\text{Average} = \frac{22 \text{ mg/L} + 30 \text{ mg/L} + 24 \text{ mg/l} + 15 \text{ mg/L}}{4} = 23 \text{ mg/L}$$

Example 2.73

Problem:

For the primary influent flow, the following composite-sampled solids concentrations were recorded for the week:

Monday	300 mg/L SS
Tuesday	312 mg/L SS
Wednesday	315 mg/L SS
Thursday	320 mg/L SS
Friday	311 mg/L SS
Saturday	320 mg/L SS
Sunday	310 mg/L SS
Total	2188 mg/L SS

What is the average solids concentration for the week?

Solution:

$$\text{Average SS} = \frac{\text{Sum of All Measurements}}{\text{Number of Measurements Used}}$$

$$= \frac{2188 \text{ mg/L SS}}{7}$$

$$= 312.6 \text{ mg/L SS}$$

2.14.1.14 Percent Removal

Percent Removal is used throughout the wastewater treatment plant to express or evaluate the performance of the plant and individual treatment unit processes. The results can be used to determine if the plant is performing as expected or in troubleshooting unit operations by comparing the results with those listed in the plant's Operations and Maintenance Manual. It can be used with either concentration or quantities (see equations 2.46 and 2.47).

For concentrations use:

$$\% \text{ Removal} = \frac{(\text{Influent Conc.} - \text{Effluent Conc.}) \times 100}{\text{Influent Conc.}} \quad (2.46)$$

For quantities use:

$$\% \text{ Removal} = \frac{(\text{Influent Quantity} - \text{Effluent Quantity}) \times 100}{\text{Influent Quantity}} \quad (2.47)$$

✓ *Note*: The calculation used for determining the performance (percent removal) for a digester is different from that used for performance (percent removal) for other processes, such as some process residuals or biosolids treatment processes. Ensure the right formula is selected.

Example 2.74

Problem:

The plant influent contains 279 mg/L BOD_5 and the plant effluent contains 17 mg/L BOD_5. What is the % BOD_5 Removal?

Solution:

$$\% \text{ Removal} = \frac{(279 \text{ mg/L} - 17 \text{ mg/L}) \times 100}{279 \text{ mg/L}}$$

$$= 93.9\%$$

2.14.1.15 Hydraulic Detention Time

The term, *detention time* or *hydraulic detention time* (HDT), refers to the average length of time (theoretical time) a drop of water, wastewater, or suspended particles remains in a tank or channel. It is calculated by dividing the water/wastewater in the tank by the flow rate through the tank. The units of flow rate used in the calculation are dependent on whether the detention time is to be calculated in seconds, minutes, hours or days. Detention time is used in conjunction with various treatment processes, including sedimentation and coagulation-flocculation.

Generally, in practice, detention time is associated with the amount of time required for a tank to empty. The range of detention time varies with the process. For example, in a tank used for sedimentation, detention time is commonly measured in minutes.

The calculation methods used to determine detention time are illustrated in the following sections.

2.14.1.15.1 Detention Time in Days

The general hydraulic detention time calculation is:

$$HDT = \frac{\text{Tank Volume}}{\text{Flow Rate}} \qquad (2.48)$$

This general formula is then modified based upon the information provided/available and the "normal" range of detention times for the unit being evaluated. Equation 2.49 shows another form of the general equation.

$$HDT, \text{Days} = \frac{\text{Tank Volume, ft}^3 \times 7.48 \text{ gal/ft}^3}{\text{Flow, gallons/day}} \qquad (2.49)$$

Example 2.75

Using the general equation (2.49)

Problem:

An anaerobic digester has a volume of 2,400,000 gallons. What is the detention time in days when the influent flow rate is 0.06 MGD?

Solution:

$$\text{D.T., Days} = \frac{2,400,000 \text{ gallons}}{0.06 \text{ MGD} \times 1,000,000 \text{ gallon/MG}} = 40 \text{ days}$$

2.14.1.15.2 Detention Time in Hours

$$\text{HDT, Hours} = \frac{\text{Tank Volume, ft}^3 \times 7.48 \text{ gal/ft}^3 \times 24 \text{ hours/day}}{\text{Flow, gallons/day}} \quad (2.50)$$

Example 2.76

Problem:

A settling tank has a volume of 40,000 ft³. What is the detention time in hours when the flow is 4.35 MGD?

Solution:

$$\text{D.T., Hours} = \frac{40,000 \text{ ft}^3 \times 7.48 \text{ gal/ft}^3 \times 24 \text{ hr/day}}{4.35 \text{ MGD} \times 1,000,000 \text{ gal/MG}}$$

$$= 1.7 \text{ hours}$$

2.14.1.15.3 Detention Time in Minutes

$$\text{HDT, minutes} = \frac{\text{Tank Volume, ft}^3 \times 7.48 \text{ gal/ft}^3 \times 1,440 \text{ minutes/day}}{\text{Flow, gallons/day}} \quad (2.51)$$

Example 2.77

Problem:

A grit channel has a volume of 1,240 ft³. What is the detention time in minutes, when the flow rate is 4.1 MGD?

Solution:

$$\text{D.T., Minutes} = \frac{1,240 \text{ ft}^3 \times 7.48 \text{ gal/ft}^3 \times 1,440 \text{ min/day}}{4,100,000 \text{ gallons/day}}$$

$$= 3.26 \text{ minutes}$$

✓ *Note*: The tank volume and the flow rate must be in the same dimensions before calculating the hydraulic detention time.

2.14.1.16 Population Equivalent (PE) or Unit Loading Factor

When it is impossible to conduct a wastewater characterization study and other data are unavailable, population equivalent or unit per capita loading factors are used to estimate the total waste loadings to be treated. If the BOD contribution of a discharger is known, the loading placed upon the wastewater treatment system in terms of equivalent number of people can be determined. The BOD contribution of a person is normally assumed to be 0.17 lbs BOD/day.

$$\text{P.E., people} = \frac{\text{BOD}_5 \text{ Contribution, lbs/day}}{0.17 \text{ lbs BOD}_5/\text{Day/person}} \qquad (2.52)$$

Example 2.78

Problem:

A new industry wishes to connect to the city's collection system. The industrial discharge will contain an average BOD concentration of 349 mg/L and the average daily flow will be 50,000 gallons per day. What is the population equivalent of the industrial discharge?

Solution:

First, convert flow rate to million gallons per day:

$$\text{Flow} = \frac{50,000 \text{ gpd}}{1,000,000 \text{ gal/MG}} = 0.050 \text{ MGD}$$

Next calculate the population equivalent:

$$\text{P.E., people} = \frac{349 \text{ mg/L} \times 0.050 \text{ MGD} \times 8.34 \text{ lbs/mg/L/MG}}{0.17 \text{ lbs BOD/person/day}}$$

$$= 856 \text{ people/day}$$

2.14.1.17 Specific Gravity

Specific gravity is the ratio of the density of a substance to that of a standard material under standard conditions of temperature and pressure. The standard material for gases is air; the standard material for liquids and solids is water. Specific gravity can be used to calculate the weight of a gallon of liquid chemical.

$$\text{Chemical, lb/gal.} \div \text{Water, lb/gal.} = \text{Chemical's Specific Gravity} \qquad (2.53)$$

Problem:

The label of the chemical states that the contents of the bottle has a specific gravity of 1.4515. What is the weight of 1 gallon of the chemical in solution?

Solution:

$$\text{Weight, lbs/gallon} = 1.4515 \times 8.34 \text{ lbs/gallon}$$

$$= 12.1 \text{ lbs}$$

2.14.1.18 Percent Volatile Matter Reduction in Sludge

The calculation used to determine *percent volatile matter reduction* is complicated because of the changes occurring during sludge digestion.

$$\% \text{ V.M. Reduction} = \frac{(\% \text{ V.M.}_{in} - \% \text{ V.M.}_{out})100}{[\% \text{ V.M.}_{in} - (\% \text{V.M.}_{in} \times \% \text{V.M.}_{out})]} \qquad (2.54)$$

✓ *Note*: V.M. = Volatile Matter

Example 2.79

Problem:

Using the digester data provided below, determine the % Volatile Matter Reduction for the digester.

Data:

Raw Sludge Volatile Matter   72%
Digested Sludge Volatile Matter   51%

$$\% \text{ Volatile Matter Reduction} = \frac{(0.72 - 0.51) \times 100}{[0.72 - (0.72 \times 0.51)]} = 59\%$$

2.14.1.19 Horsepower & Energy Costs

Horsepower is a common expression for power. One horsepower is equal to 33,000 foot pounds of work per minute. This value is derived, for example, in selection of a pump or combination of pumps with an adequate pumping capacity. This pumping capacity depends upon the flow rate desired and the feet of head against which the pump must pump (i.e., effective height).

The basic concept from which the horsepower calculation is derived is the concept of work. *Work* involves the operation of a force (lbs) over a specific distance (ft). The *amount of work* accomplished is measured in foot-pounds:

$$(ft)(lbs) = ft\text{-}lbs \tag{2.55}$$

The rate of doing work is called power. The time factor in which the work occurs now becomes important. The rate of doing work or power was compared to the power of a horse to that of the steam engine. The rate at which a horse could work was determined to be about 550 ft-lbs/sec (or expressed as 33,000 ft-lbs/min). This rate has become the definition of the standard unit called horsepower, shown in equation 2.56).

2.14.1.19.1 Horsepower

$$\text{Horsepower, hp} = \frac{\text{Power, ft-lbs/min}}{33,000 \text{ ft-lbs/min/HP}} \tag{2.56}$$

2.14.1.19.2 Water Horsepower

The amount of power required to move a given volume of water a specified total head is known as water horsepower (Whp).

$$\text{Whp} = \frac{\text{Pump Rate, gpm} \times \text{Total Head, ft} \times 8.34 \text{ lbs/gal}}{33,000 \text{ ft-lb/min/hp}} \tag{2.57}$$

Example 2.80

Problem:

A pump must deliver 1,240 gpm to total head of 140 feet. What is the required water horsepower?

Solution:

$$\text{Whp} = \frac{1{,}240 \text{ gpm} \times 140 \text{ ft} \times 8.34 \text{ lbs/gal}}{33{,}000 \text{ ft-lbs/minute}} = 44 \text{ Whp}$$

2.14.1.19.3 Brake Horsepower

Brake horsepower (*bhp*) refers to the horsepower supplied to the pump from the motor. As power moves through the pump, additional horsepower is lost, resulting from slippage and friction of the shaft and other factors; thus, pump efficiencies range from about 50 to 85%. The efficiency of the pump must be taken into account.

$$\text{Bhp} = \frac{\text{Whp}}{\text{Pump \% Efficiency}} \qquad (2.58)$$

Example 2.81

Problem:

Under the specified conditions, the pump efficiency is 73%. If the required water horsepower is 50 hp, what is the required brake horsepower?

Solution:

$$\text{Bhp} = \frac{50 \text{ Whp}}{0.73} = 68 \text{ Bhp}$$

2.14.1.19.4 Motor Horsepower

Motor horsepower is the horsepower of the motor necessary to produce the desired brake and water horsepower.

$$\text{Mhp} = \frac{\text{Brake Horsepower, Bhp}}{\text{Motor \% Efficiency}} \qquad (2.59)$$

Problem:

The motor is 93% efficient. What is the required motor horsepower when the required brake horsepower is 49.0 Bhp?

Solution:

$$\text{Mhp} = \frac{49.0 \text{ Bhp}}{0.93} = 53 \text{ Mhp}$$

2.14.1.20 Electrical Power

On occasion, wastewater operators (especially senior operators) are required to make electrical power calculations—especially in regard to electrical energy required/consumed during a period of time. To accomplish this, horsepower is converted to electrical energy (kilowatts), and then multiplied by the hours of operation to obtain kilowatt hours.

$$\text{Kilowatt-Hours} = \text{Hp} \times 0.746 \text{ kw/hp} \times \text{Operating Time, hrs} \quad (2.60)$$

Example 2.82

Problem:

An 80-horsepower motor operates at full load 12 hours per day (seven days per week). How many kilowatts of energy does it consume per day?

Solution:

$$\text{Kilowatt-hours/day} = 80 \text{ hp} \times 0.746 \text{ kw/hp} \times 12 \text{ hours/day}$$
$$= 716 \text{ kw-hr/day}$$

Given the cost per kilowatt hour, the operator may calculate the cost of power for any given period of operation.

$$\text{Cost} = \text{Power Required/Day, kw-hr/day} \times \text{Days/Period} \times \text{Cost/kw-hr} \quad (2.61)$$

Example 2.83

Problem:

A 60-horsepower motor requires 458 kw-hr/day. The pump is in operation every day. The current cost of electricity is $0.0328 per kilowatt hour. What is the yearly electrical cost for this pump?

Solution:

$$\text{Cost, } \$ = 458 \text{ kw-hr/day} \times 365 \text{ days/year} \times \$0.0328/\text{kw-hr}$$
$$= \$5,483.18$$

2.14.1.21 Plant Loadings

After pretreatment is done (i.e., screenings and grit have been removed), a sample can be taken to measure the concentration of contaminants in the waste stream. One of the common tests performed measures the amount of solids that are suspended in the water. Another test measures the biological activity of the water.

2.14.1.21.1 Suspended Solids

The concentration of suspended solids in the water can be measured by pouring a wastewater sample through a paper filter placed on top of a *gooch crucible* (ceramic filter holder). Then, solids that become trapped on the paper are weighed.

Example 2.84

Problem:

A 20-milliliter (mL) sample of wastewater is filtered for a suspended solids test. The crucible with filter paper was weighed at 22.3668 grams (g). After the sample was filtered, the crucible was dried at 103°C. After cooling, the crucible with the dried solids in it was weighed at 22.3878 g. What was the concentration of suspended solids in milligrams per liter (mg/L)?

Solution:

First, find the weight of the solids in units milligrams.

Weight of crucible with dry solids	22.3878 g
Weight of crucible and filter paper	−22.3668 g
	0.021 g

Then, convert grams to mg

$$0.021 \text{ g} \times \frac{1000 \text{ mg}}{1 \text{ g}} = 21 \text{ mg}$$

The original sample was 20 mL

$$20 \text{ mL} \times \frac{1\text{L}}{1000 \text{ mL}} = 0.02 \text{ L}$$

Finally, all that is left is to divide

$$\frac{21 \text{ mg}}{0.02\text{L}} = \frac{1050 \text{ mg}}{1\text{L}} = 1050 \text{ mg/L}$$

2.14.1.21.2 Biochemical Oxygen Demand (BOD)

The wastewater operator needs to know how much biological activity there is in raw wastewater. Along with dissolved fats, proteins and other chemicals, raw wastewater contains microorganisms. As their name suggests, these microorganisms are too small to be seen by the unaided eye—a microscope must be used.

It is not necessarily important to determine what type of microorganisms live in the wastewater, but rather it is more important to determine how much oxygen they use. We measure this by conducting a *Biochemical Oxygen Demand Test* (or BOD test).

$$\text{BOD} = \text{Amount of Oxygen used by Microorganisms} \qquad (2.62)$$

$$\text{Dissolved Oxygen (DO)} = \text{Amount of Oxygen in Water} \qquad (2.63)$$

To conduct a BOD Test:

(1) Measure the oxygen of the sample
(2) Incubate the sample for five days
(3) Measure the oxygen left in the sample after 5 days

$$\text{BOD} = \text{Initial DO} - \text{Final DO} \qquad (2.64)$$

Example 2.85

Problem:

A BOD test was done on a 5 mL sample. The initial DO of the sample and dilution water was 7.82 mg/L. The DO of the sample after 5 days of incubation was 4.17 mg/L. What was the BOD of the sample?

Solution:

Initial DO   7.82 mg/L
Final DO   4.17 mg/L DO
Depletion   3.65 mg/L

The BOD bottle is 300 mL. Therefore, the sample fraction was:

$$\frac{5\ mL}{300\ mL} = 0.0167$$

$$BOD = \frac{DO\ Depletion}{Sample\ Fraction} = \frac{3.65\ mg/L}{0.0167} = 218.6\ mg/L\ (219\ mg/L)$$

2.15 KEY TERMS USED IN THIS CHAPTER

- *Area*—the surface of an object. Measured in square units.
- *Base*—the term used to identify the bottom leg of a triangle. Measured in linear units.
- *Circumference*—the distance around an object, usually a circular object. Measured in linear units. When determined for other than circles it may be called the perimeter of the figure.
- *Common factor (or common divisor)*—of two or more numbers is a factor that will exactly divide each of them. If this factor is the largest factor possible, it is called the greatest common divisor. Thus, 4 is a common divisor of 16 and 24, but 8 is greatest common divisor of 16 and 24.
- *Composite number*—a number that has factors other than itself and 1. Examples of composite numbers are 4, 6, 8, 9, and 12.
- *Cubic units*—measurements used to express volume. Cubic feet, cubic meters, etc.
- *Depth*—the vertical distance from the bottom of a tank to the top. Normally measured in terms of water depth and given in terms of side wall depth (SWD).
- *Diameter*—the distance from one edge of a circle to the opposite edge passing through the center. Measured in linear units.
- *Dividend*—a number to be divided; a divisor is a number that divides. For example, in $100 \div 25 = 4$, 100 is the dividend, 25 is the divisor, and 4 is the quotient.
- *Even number*—a number exactly divisible by 2. 2, 4, 6, 8, 10, and 12 are each an *Integer*—a whole number. Thus, 1, 2, 3, 4, 5, 6, 7, 8, 9, 10, 11, 12 are the first twelve positive integers.

- *Factor (or divisor)*—of a whole number is any other whole number that exactly divides it. Thus, 3 and 4 are factors of 12.
- *Height*—the vertical distance from the base of bottom of a unit to the top or water surface.
- *Length*—the distance from one end of the tank to the other. Measured in linear units.
- *Linear units*—measurements used to express distances (e.g., feet, inches, meters, etc.)
- *Multiple*—of a given number is a number that is exactly divisible by the given number. If a number is exactly divisible by two or more other numbers, that number is their common multiple. The least (smallest) such number is called the lowest common multiple. Thus, 36 and 72 are common multiples of 12, 9, and 4; however, 36 is the lowest common multiple.
- *Odd number*—an integer that is not exactly divisible by 2. 1, 3, 5, 7, 9, or 11 are odd integers.
- *Pi, π*—a Greek letter with a numerical value of 3.1416 representing the ratio of the circumference of a circle to its diameter. It is used in many calculations involving circles.
- *Prime Number*—a number that has no factors except itself and 1. Examples of prime numbers are 1, 3, 5, 7, and 11.even integers.
- *Product*—the result of multiplying two or more numbers together. Thus, 21 is the product of 3×7, and 3 and 7 are factors of 21.
- *Quotient*—the result of dividing one number by another. For example, 7 is the quotient of 21 divided by 3.
- *Radius*—the distance from the center of a circle to the edge. Measured in linear units.
- *Sphere*—a container shaped like a ball.
- *Square units*—measurements used to express areas. Square feet, square meters, acres, etc.
- *Volume*—the capacity of the unit. How much it will hold. Measured in cubic units (cubic feet, cubic meters) or in liquid volume units (gallons, liters, million gallons).
- *Width*—the distance from one side of the tank to the other. Measured in linear units.

2.16 CHAPTER 2 SELF-TEST

2-1 $[(25 - 4 - 6) \div (3 \times 5)] + 4 \times 3 =$

2-2 $(720 \div 360) + (180 \times 2) + 1 =$

2-3 2/3 is equal to how many ninths (?/9)

2-4 3/4 × 5/6 =

2-5 3/7 × 2/3 =

2-6 2/3 + 3/4 =

2-7 What is the fraction equivalent of 0.625?

2-8 What is the decimal equivalent of 3/4?

2-9 What is 1/3 × 15% of 0.75 × 5/3?

2-10 What is the MEAN and the MEDIAN of 3, 5, 6, 8, 11, 17?

2-11 Write 10,000,000 as a power of ten.

2-12 How many liters can a 250-gallon tank hold?

2-13 What is the area of a rectangle 9 ft by 30 ft?

2-14 What is the volume of a tank 25 ft × 60 ft × 8 ft deep?

2-15 What is the volume of a round tank 10 ft deep, with a 35 ft diameter?

2-16 A pipe has a diameter of 8 inches. Water is flowing through it at 4 feet per minute. How much water is passing through in one minute? In one hour?

2-17 Find the volume of a fuel tank 5 feet in diameter and 12 feet long.

2-18 Find the volume of a chlorine cylinder that is 25 inches in diameter and 44 inches tall.

2-19 The average day winter demand of a community is 14,000 gallons. If the summer demand is estimated to be 73% greater than the winter, what is the estimated summer demand?

✓ *Note:* Demand is the amount of water used in a period of time. The term is in reference to the "demand" put onto the system to meet the need of customers.

2-20 Convert 50 gallons to pounds.

2-21 Convert 135 ft^3 of water to weight in pounds.

2-22 A reservoir is 40 feet deep. What will the pressure be at the bottom of the reservoir?

2-23 Find the flow in gpm when the flow is 1.5 cfs.

2-24 The sedimentation basin of a waterworks contains 6,575 gallons. What is the detention time if the flow is 160 gpm?

2-25 The depth of water the grit channel is 40 inches. What is the depth in feet?

2-26 The operator withdraws 5,450 gallons of solids from the digester. How many pounds of solids have been removed?

2-27 The plant effluent contains 38 mg/L solids. The effluent flow rate is 3.89 MGD. How many pounds per day of solids are discharged?

2-28 The plant effluent contains 26 mg/L of BOD_5. The effluent flow rate is 7.25 MGD. How many kilograms per day of BOD_5 are being discharged?

2-29 The operator wishes to remove 3,540 pounds per day of solids from the activated sludge process. The waste activated sludge concentration is 3,524 mg/L. What is the required flow rate in million gallons per day?

2-30 A gallon of solution is weighed. After the weight of the container is subtracted, it is determined that the weight of the solution is 8.5 lbs. What is the density of the solution?

2-31 The density of a liquid is given at 45 lbs/cu ft. What is the specific gravity of the liquid?

2-32 A pump must pump 1,800 gpm against a total head of 30 ft. What hp is required for this work?

2-33 The digester has a diameter of 60 feet and is 26 feet deep. If the operator pumps 5,200 gallons of residuals (sludge) to the digester per day. What is the hydraulic detention time in the digester in days?

CHAPTER 3

Wastewater Sources and Characteristics

Describe all the forms taken by water from its greatest to smallest wave, and their causes. (Leonardo da Vinci, Notebooks)

3.1 SOURCES OF WASTEWATER

WASTEWATER is the flow of used water from a community. The characteristics of the wastewater discharges will vary from location to location depending upon the population and industrial sector served, land uses, groundwater levels, and degree of separation between stormwater and sanitary wastes.

As shown in Figure 3.1, wastewater is generated by five major sources. Each source produces wastewater with specific characteristics.

3.1.1 HUMAN AND ANIMAL WASTES

Human and animal wastes comprise the solid and liquid discharges of humans and animals. This waste contains millions of bacteria, viruses and other organisms some of which may be pathogenic. Consequently, from a human health point of view, human and animal wastes are considered by many to be the most dangerous.

3.1.2 HOUSEHOLD WASTES

Waterborne wastes, other than human and animal wastes, discharged from the home are called household wastes. Household wastes contain paper, household cleaners, detergents, trash, garbage, and any other substance the average home occupant may discharge to the sewer system.

91

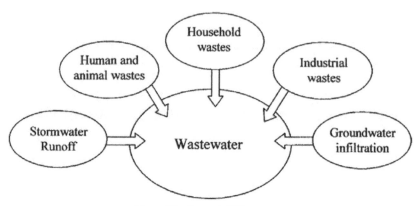

Figure 3.1. Sources of Wastewater.

3.1.3 INDUSTRIAL WASTES

Industrial wastes include all materials discharged from industrial process-es into the collection system. These wastes are industry specific; that is, they may include chemicals, dyes, acids, alkalis, grit, detergents, and highly toxic materials specific to the industry and processes used.

3.1.4 STORMWATER RUNOFF

Some collection systems are designed to convey both the wastes of the community and stormwater runoff. If this is the case, wastewater can, during and after a storm event, contain large amounts of sand, gravel and other grit as well as excessive amounts of water.

3.1.5 GROUNDWATER INFILTRATION

In aging collection systems, it is not unusual (or unexpected) for ground-water to enter the system through cracks, breaks or unsealed joints. This can add large amounts of water to the wastewater flows as well as additional grit.

3.2 TYPES OF WASTEWATER

Generally, wastewater is classified according to the sources of the flows (see Figure 3.2).

3.2.1 DOMESTIC WASTEWATER (SEWAGE)

Domestic wastewater includes typical wastes from the kitchen, bathroom, and laundry, as well as any other wastes that people may accidentally or intentionally pour down the drain. Though consisting mainly of these wastes, small amounts of groundwater infiltration and small amounts of industrial wastes may also be present.

3.2.2 SANITARY WASTEWATER

Sanitary wastewater consist of domestic wastewater as well as wastewater discharged from commercial, institutional, and similar facilities.

✓ *Note:* In some cases the industrial wastes in sanitary wastewater will require special precautions or a pretreatment program to ensure the wastes do not cause compliance problems for the plant.

3.2.3 INDUSTRIAL WASTEWATER

Many industries treat their own wastewater. This is the case primarily because of economics. For example, industrial waste added to a community-owned collection system can be extremely expensive to treat, not only for the treatment plant but also in the fees paid by the industrial waste contributor.

3.2.4 COMBINED WASTEWATER

Combined wastewater is a combination of sanitary wastewater and the storm-water runoff transported through one system. The quantities of storm-water that combines with the domestic wastewater will vary with the degree of operation that exists between the storm sewers and the sanitary sewers.

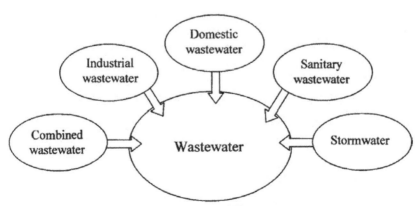

Figure 3.2. Types of Wastewater.

3.2.5 STORMWATER

Most new sewerage systems are separate, collecting either sanitary wastewater or storm wastes, whereas the older combined systems (as mentioned in Section 3.2.4) collect both sanitary wastewater and stormwater. The flow in the stormwater system should contain grit and street debris but no domestic or sanitary wastes.

3.3 WASTEWATER CHARACTERISTICS

Because wastewater contains many different substances, it is characterized by its physical, chemical and biological aspects. Depending on the source, the specific substances present will vary, as will the amounts or concentrations of each. For this reason wastewater characteristics are normally described for an "average domestic" wastewater. Other sources and types of wastewater can dramatically change the characteristics.

3.3.1 PHYSICAL CHARACTERISTICS

Physically, wastewater is characterized by color, odor, temperature, flow, and solids content.

3.3.1.1 Color

Wastewater is usually characterized by a gray color and cloudy appearance. The color of the wastewater will change significantly if allowed to go septic. Typical septic wastewater will have a black color.

3.3.1.2 Odor

Fresh domestic wastewater has a musty odor. This odor will change significantly if the wastewater is allowed to become septic. The wastewater will have the rotten egg odor associated with hydrogen sulfide production.

3.3.1.3 Temperature

The wastewater temperature will normally be close to that of the water supply. Significant amounts of infiltration or stormwater flow can cause major temperature changes.

3.3.1.4 Flow

The volume of wastewater is normally expressed in terms of gallons per person per day. Most treatment facilities are designed using an expected flow of 100 to 200 gallons per person per day. This figure may have to be revised to reflect the degree of infiltration or storm flow the plant receives. Flow rates will vary throughout the day. This variation, which can be as much as 50 to 200% of the average daily flow, is known as the diurnal flow variation.

3.3.1.5 Solids Content

Wastewater has a solids content of about 0.1%, and a 99.9% water content. The solids can be suspended (about 30%) as well as dissolved (about 70%). Dissolved solids can be precipitated by chemical and biological processes. From a physical point of view the suspended solids can lead to the development of sludge deposits and anaerobic conditions when discharged into the receiving environment.

3.3.2 CHEMICAL CHARACTERISTICS

Chemically, wastewater is composed of organic and inorganic compounds as well as various gases. Organic compounds may include carbohydrates, proteins, fats and greases, surfactants, oils, pesticides, phenols, etc. Inorganic components may be heavy metals, nitrogen, phosphorus, pH, sulfur, chlorides, alkalinity, toxic compounds, etc. In domestic wastewater, the organic and inorganic portions are approximately 50% each. However, since wastewater contains a higher portion of dissolved solids than suspended, about 85 to 90% of the total inorganic component is dissolved. Gases commonly dissolved in wastewater are hydrogen sulfide, methane, ammonia, oxygen, carbon dioxide and nitrogen. The first three gases result from the decomposition of organic matter present in the wastewater.

3.3.2.1 Chemical Parameters

Several chemical parameters are used to characterize wastewater.

3.3.2.1.1 Alkalinity

Alkalinity is a measure of the wastewater's capability to neutralize acids. It is measured in terms of bicarbonate, carbonate and hydroxide alkalinity. Alkalinity is essential to buffer (hold the neutral pH) the wastewater during the biological treatment processes.

3.3.2.1.2 Biochemical Oxygen Demand (BOD₅)

Biochemical oxygen demand (or BOD) is a measure of the amount of biodegradable matter in the wastewater. Normally measured by a five-day test conducted at 20°C, the BOD_5 of domestic waste is normally in the range of 100 to 300 mg/L.

3.3.2.1.3 Chemical Oxygen Demand (COD)

Chemical oxygen demand (or COD) is a measure of the amount of oxidizable matter present in the sample. The COD is normally in the range of 200 to 500 mg/L. The presence of industrial wastes can increase this significantly.

3.3.2.1.4 Dissolved Gases

The specific dissolved gases and normal concentrations in wastewater are based upon the composition of the wastewater. Typical domestic wastewater contains oxygen (in relatively low concentrations), carbon dioxide, and hydrogen sulfide (if septic conditions exist).

3.3.2.1.5 Nitrogen Compounds

The type and amount of nitrogen present will vary from the raw wastewater to the treated effluent. Nitrogen follows a cycle of oxidation and reduction. Most of the nitrogen in untreated wastewater will be in the forms of organic nitrogen and ammonia nitrogen. Laboratory tests exist for determination of both of these forms. The sum of these two forms of nitrogen is also measured and is known as Total Kjeldahl Nitrogen (TKN). Wastewater will normally contain 20 to 85 mg/L of nitrogen. Organic nitrogen will normally be in the range of 8 to 35 mg/L, and ammonia nitrogen will be in the range of 12 to 50 mg/L.

3.3.2.1.6 pH

pH is a method of expressing the acid condition of the wastewater. pH is expressed on a scale of 1 to 14. For proper treatment wastewater pH should normally be in the range of 6.5 to 9.0 (6.5 to 8.0 ideal; see Figure 3.3).

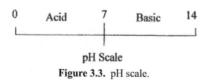

Figure 3.3. pH scale.

3.3.2.1.7 Phosphorus

Phosphorus is essential to biological activity and must be present in at least minimum quantities or secondary treatment processes will not perform. Excessive amounts can cause stream damage and overly abundant algal growth. Phosphorus will normally be in the range of 6 to 20 mg/L. The removal of phosphate compounds from detergents has had a significant impact on the amounts of phosphorus in the wastewater.

3.3.2.1.8 Solids

Most contaminants found in wastewater can be classified as solids. Wastewater treatment is generally designed to remove solids or to convert solids to a form that is more stable that can be removed. Solids can be classified by their chemical composition (organic or inorganic) or by their physical characteristics (settleable, floatable, colloidal). Concentration of total solids in wastewater is normally in the range of 350 to 1,200 mg/L.

(1) *Organic solids*—consist of compounds of carbon, hydrogen, oxygen, nitrogen and can be converted to carbon dioxide and water by ignition at 550°C. Also known as volatile solids or loss on ignition.

(2) *Inorganic solids*—mineral solids (also known as fixed solids or ash) that are unaffected by ignition.

(3) *Suspended solids*—will not pass through a glass fiber filter pad. Can be further classified as Total Suspended Solids (TSS), Volatile Suspended Solids and/or Fixed Suspended Solids. Can also be separated into three components based on settling characteristics: settleable solids, floatable solids and colloidal solids. Total suspended solids in wastewater is normally in the range of 100 to 350 mg/L.

(4) *Dissolved Solids*—will pass through a glass fiber filter pad. Can also be classified as Total Dissolved Solids (TDS), volatile dissolved solids, and fixed dissolved solids. Total dissolved solids is normally in the range of 250 to 850 mg/L.

3.3.2.1.9 Water

Always the major component, in most cases water makes up 99.5 to 99.9% of the wastewater. Even in the strongest wastewater, the total amount of contamination present is less than 0.5% of the total, and in average-strength wastes it is normally less than 0.1%.

3.3.3 BIOLOGICAL CHARACTERISTICS

Biologically, wastewater contains various microorganisms, but the ones of concern are those classified as protista, plants, and animals. In terms of wastewater treatment, the most important category is the protista, especially the bacteria and protozoa. Also, wastewater contains many pathogenic organisms, which generally originate from humans who are infected with disease or who are carriers of a particular disease. Since the identification of pathogenic organisms in water and wastewater is very time consuming and difficult, the coliform group of organisms that are more numerous and more easily tested for, is used as an indicator of the presence of pathogenic organisms. However, coliform testing does not accurately reflect the presence or absence of all pathogens that may be found in the treated effluent, e.g., viruses. Typically, the concentration of fecal coliforms found in raw wastewater is about several hundred thousand to tens of million per 100 mL of sample.

In order to have biological activity in wastewater treatment plant operations, appropriate environmental conditions must be present. The majority of wastewater unit processes are designed to operate using an aerobic process. The conditions required for aerobic treatment are:

- sufficient oxygen
- sufficient organic matter (food)
- sufficient water
- nutrients (nitrogen and phosphorus)
- proper pH (6.5 to 9.0)
- lack of toxic materials

3.3.3.1 Bacteria

Bacteria are microscopic prokaryotes present in all human and animal body discharges. Of all the microorganisms present in wastewater, they are the most widely distributed, the smallest in size, the simplest in morphology (structure), the most difficult to classify, and the hardest to identify. Bacteria can be classified in many different ways including the sources of oxygen and the processes they use to survive (aerobic, anaerobic, anoxic, facultative); their ability to cause disease (pathogenic or non-pathogenic); their shape and many other characteristics (see Figure 3.4). Not only are bacteria present in wastewater, they are also the main workers in the process to remove contaminants from the water (i.e., they eat the contaminants).

3.3.3.2 Protozoa

The protozoa ("first animals") are microscopic animals that are a higher life

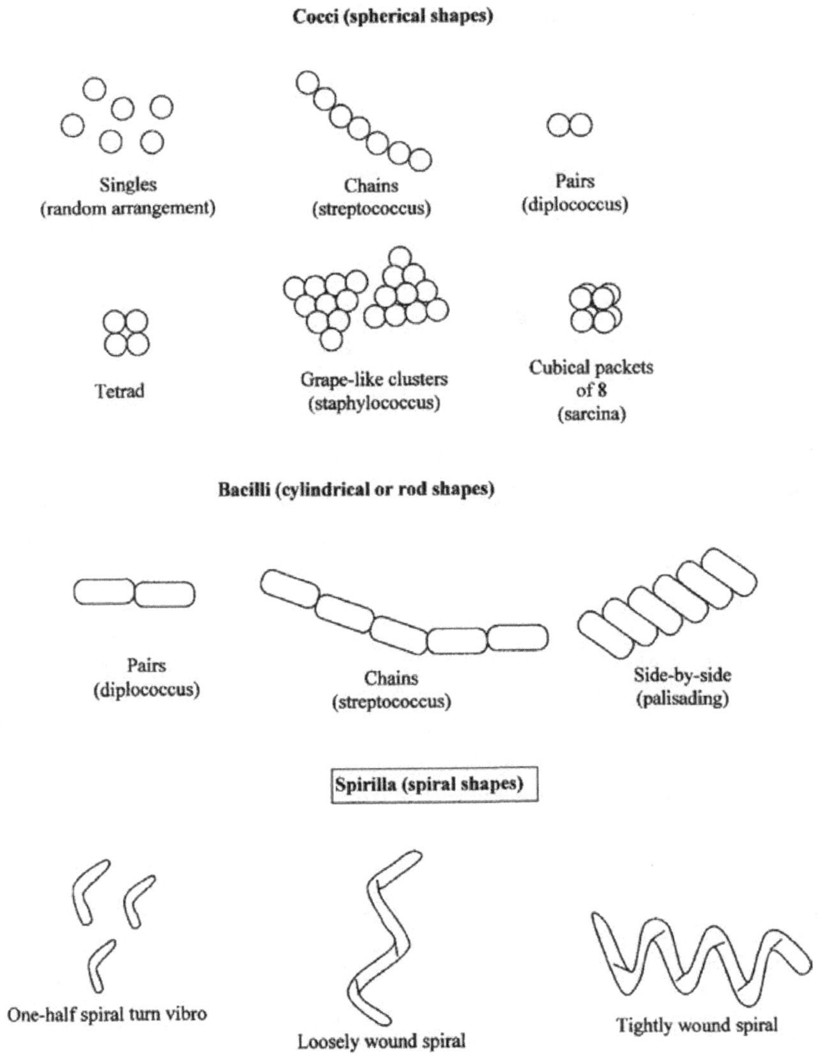

Cocci (spherical shapes)

Singles
(random arrangement)

Chains
(streptococcus)

Pairs
(diplococcus)

Tetrad

Grape-like clusters
(staphylococcus)

Cubical packets
of 8
(sarcina)

Bacilli (cylindrical or rod shapes)

Pairs
(diplococcus)

Chains
(streptococcus)

Side-by-side
(palisading)

Spirilla (spiral shapes)

One-half spiral turn vibro

Loosely wound spiral

Tightly wound spiral

Figure 3.4. Bacterial shapes and arrangements.

form than bacteria and are normally associated with less polluted waters. They are a critical part of the purification process and can be used to indicate the condition of treatment processes. Protozoans normally associated with wastewater include amoebas, flagellates, free-swimming ciliates, and stalked ciliates.

3.3.3.2.1 Amoeba

Amoebas (see Figure 3.5) are associated with poor treatment or a young

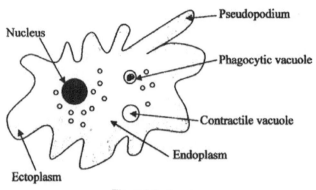

Figure 3.5. Amoeba.

sludge (biomass). Amoebas move through the wastewater by moving the liquids stored within their cell wall. They are normally associated with treatment that produces an effluent high in BOD_5 and suspended solids.

3.3.3.2.2 Flagellates

Flagellated protozoans have a single, long, hair-like projection (flagellum), which is used to propel the organism through the wastewater and to attract food (see Figure 3.6). Flagellated protozoans are normally associated with poor treatment and a young sludge (biomass). When they predominate, plant effluent will contain large amounts of BOD_5 and suspended solids.

3.3.3.2.3 Free-Swimming Ciliates

Paramecium and Euplotes shown in Figure 3.7 are two examples of free-swimming ciliates typically found in wastewater. Free-swimming ciliated protozoans use tiny, hair-like projections (cilia) to move themselves through the wastewater and to attract food. Free-swimming ciliated protozoans are normally associated with a moderate sludge age and effluent quality. When they predominate, plant effluent will normally be turbid and contain a high amount of suspended solids.

Flagella

Figure 3.6. Flagellate protozoa.

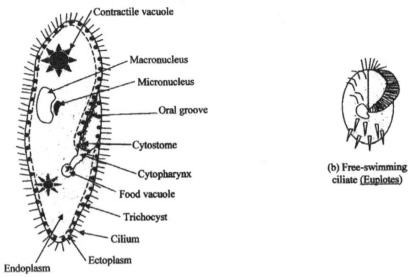

Figure 3.7. Drawings show (a) free-swimming cilate, Paramecium; (b) free-swimming cilate, Euplotes.

3.3.3.2.4 Stalked Ciliates

Stalked-ciliated protozoans attach themselves to wastewater solids and use their cilia to attract food (see Figure 3.8). They are normally associated with a plant effluent that is very clear and contains low amounts of both BOD_5 and suspended solids.

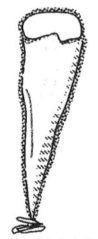

Figure 3.8. Stalked ciliate.

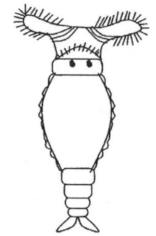

Figure 3.9. Philodina, a common rotifer.

3.3.3.3 Rotifers

Rotifers make up a well-defined group of the smallest, simplest multicellular microorganisms and are found in nearly all aquatic habitats. Often associated with aerobic biological processes in wastewater treatment plants, they are seen either grazing on bacteria or attached to debris by their forked tail or toe (see Figure 3.9). Rotifers promote microfloral activity and decomposition, enhance oxygen penetration in activated sludge and trickling filters, and recycle minerals in each. Accordingly, rotifers play an important part in well-operated wastewater unit processes such as activated sludge, trickling filters, and oxidation pond systems. Indeed, rotifers are often used to indicate the performance of certain unit processes.

3.4 WASTEWATER HYDRAULICS

The study of how the flow of wastewater acts as it moves through a channel or a pipe is known as wastewater hydraulics. Hydraulics plays an important role in the design and operation of both the wastewater collection system and treatment plant. The following sections present information about several basic concepts of wastewater hydraulics.

3.4.1 HEAD

Head is the vertical distance wastewater must be lifted from the supply source to the discharge. The total head includes the vertical distance the liquid must be lifted (static head), the loss to friction (friction head), and the energy required to maintain the desired velocity (velocity head).

$$\text{Total Head} = \text{Static Head} + \text{Friction Head} + \text{Velocity Head} \qquad (3.1)$$

✓ *Note:* All parameters shown in equation (3.1) are in feet.

3.4.1.1 Static Head

✓ *Note:* In the following sections, Figure 3.10 is provided to indicate and illustrate the various parameters discussed.

Static head is the actual vertical distance the liquid must be lifted (see Figure 3.10).

$$\text{Static Head} = \text{Discharge Elevation} - \text{Supply Elevation} \qquad (3.2)$$

Example 3.1

Problem:

The supply tank is located at an elevation of 120 feet. The discharge is at an elevation of 210 feet. What is the static head in feet?

Solution:

$$\text{Static head} = 210 \text{ feet} - 120 \text{ feet} = 90 \text{ feet}$$

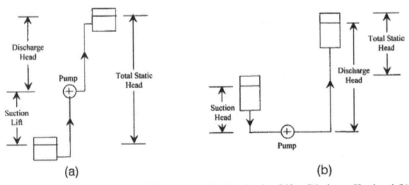

Figure 3.10. Total static head: (a) Total Static Head = Suction Lift + Discharge Head and (b) Total Static Head = Discharge Head + Suction Head.

3.4.1.2 Friction Head

Friction head is the equivalent distance of the energy that must be supplied to overcome friction. The total friction head is the sum of the equivalent vertical distances for each component.

✓ *Note:* Engineering references include tables showing the equivalent vertical distance for various sizes and types of pipes, fittings, and valves.

$$\text{Friction head} = \text{Energy losses due to friction} \qquad (3.3)$$

3.4.1.3 Velocity Head

Velocity head is the equivalent distance of the energy consumed in achieving and maintaining the desired velocity in the system.

$$\text{Velocity head} = \text{Energy losses to maintain velocity} \qquad (3.4)$$

3.4.1.4 Total Dynamic Head (Total System Head)

Total dynamic head is the total of the static head, friction head, and velocity head.

$$\text{Total Head} = \text{Static Head} + \text{Friction Head} + \text{Velocity Head} \qquad (3.5)$$

3.4.2 PRESSURE/HEAD

Pressure exerted by wastewater is directly proportional to its depth or head in the pipe, channel or tank. If the pressure is known, the equivalent head can be calculated.

$$\text{Pressure, psi} = \frac{\text{Head, ft}}{2.31 \text{ ft/psi}} \qquad (3.6)$$

Example 3.2

Problem:

The pressure gauge on the discharge line from the influent pump read 71.5 psi. What is the equivalent head in feet?

Solution:

$$\text{Head, ft} = 71.5 \text{ psi} \times 2.31 \text{ ft/psi} = 165.2 \text{ ft}$$

3.4.3 HEAD/PRESSURE

If the head is known, the equivalent pressure can be calculated.

$$\text{Pressure, psi} = \frac{\text{Head, ft}}{2.31 \text{ ft/psi}} \qquad (3.6)$$

Example 3.3

Problem:

The tank is fourteen feet deep. What is the pressure in psi at the bottom of the tank when it is filled with wastewater?

$$\text{Pressure, psi} = \frac{14 \text{ ft}}{2.31 \text{ ft/psi}} = 6.1 \text{ psi}$$

3.4.4 FLOW, AREA, VELOCITY

The flow rate through an open channel is directly related to the velocity of the liquid and the cross-sectional area of the liquid in the channel.

$$\text{Flow } (Q), \text{ cfs} = A, \text{ ft}^2 \times v, \text{ fps} \qquad (3.7)$$

where

Q = flow
A = cross-sectional area of liquid
v = velocity

Example 3.4

Problem:

The channel is 5 feet wide and the water depth is 2 feet. The velocity in the channel is 3 feet per second. What is the flow rate in cubic feet per second?

Solution:

$$\text{Flow, cfs} = 5 \text{ ft} \times 2 \text{ ft} \times 3 \text{ ft/sec} = 30 \text{ cfs}$$

3.4.5 AREA/VELOCITY

At a given flow rate the velocity of the liquid varies indirectly with changes in cross-sectional area of the channel or pipe. This principle provides the basis for many of the flow measurement devices used in open channels (e.g., weirs, flumes, nozzles).

$$\text{Velocity}_1 \times \text{Area}_1 = \text{Velocity}_2 \times \text{Area}_2 \ \text{ft}^2 \qquad (3.9)$$

3.4.6 PRESSURE/VELOCITY

In a closed pressurized pipe flowing full, the pressure is indirectly related to the velocity of the wastewater. This principle forms the basis for several flow measurement devices (e.g., Venturi meters, rotameters, etc.) as well as injectors used for injecting chlorine, sulfur dioxide and other chemicals into wastewater.

$$\text{Velocity}_1 \times \text{Pressure}_1 = \text{Velocity}_2 \times \text{Pressure}_2 \qquad (3.10)$$

3.5 KEY TERMS USED IN THIS CHAPTER

- *Aerobic process*—microorganisms use free, elemental oxygen and organic matter together with nutrients (nitrogen, phosphorus) and trace metals (e.g., iron) to produce more organisms, stable dissolved and suspended solids and carbon dioxide.
- *Anaerobic Process*—consists of two steps, occurs completely in the absence of oxygen and produces a useable by-product, methane gas.
- *Friction head*—the energy needed to overcome friction in a piping system. It is expressed in terms of the added system head required.
- *Head*—the equivalent distance water must be lifted to move from a supply tank or inlet to the discharge. Head can be divided into three components, static head, velocity head, and friction head.
- *Pressure*—the force exerted per square unit of surface area. May be expressed as pounds per square inch.
- *Static head*—the actual vertical distance from the system inlet to the highest discharge point.

- *Total dynamic head*—the total of the static head, friction head, and velocity head.
- *Velocity*—the speed of a liquid moving through a pipe, channel or tank. May be expressed in feet per second.
- *Velocity head*—the energy needed to keep the liquid moving at a given velocity. It is expressed in terms of the added system head required.

3.6 CHAPTER 3 SELF-TEST

3-1 Name three sources of wastewater and give an example of the types of materials associated with each.

3-2 Name four types of microorganisms that may be present in wastewater.

3-3 List three things that must be present for good biological activity in wastewater treatment.

3-4 What is stormwater runoff and how can it cause problems for the wastewater treatment plant?

3-5 Name three types of wastewater based upon the types of waste carried.

3-6 Which type of organism is considered the most dangerous from a human health viewpoint?

3-7 Define BOD_5?

3-8 Give three reasons for treating wastewater.

3-9 The elevation of the liquid in the supply tank is 2,250 ft. The elevation of the liquid surface of the discharge tank is 2,350 ft. What is the total static head of the system?

3-10 The channel is 4 feet wide and the liquid depth in the channel is 18 inches. The measured velocity of the flow in the channel is 1.3 feet per second. What is the flow rate in million gallons per day?

CHAPTER 4

Preliminary Treatment

*The society which scorns excellence in plumbing as a humble activity and toler-
ates shoddiness in philosophy because it is an exalted activity will have neither
good plumbing nor good philosophy . . . neither its pipes nor its theories will
hold water. (John W. Gardner)*

4.1 THE FIRST STEP

*P*RELIMINARY TREATMENT screens out, grinds up, or separates debris in
the first step in the wastewater treatment process. Sticks, rags, large
food particles, sand, gravel, toys, plastics, and other objects are removed at
this stage to conserve valuable space within the treatment processes and to
protect pumping and other equipment from clogs, jams or excessive wear.
Treatment equipment such as bar screens, comminutors (a large version of
a garbage disposal that shreds materials), and grit chambers are used on the
wastewater as it first enters a treatment plant. The collected debris is usually
disposed of in a landfill.

The major unit processes are shown in Figure 4.1. In this chapter, we describe and discuss each of these processes and their importance in the treatment process.

✓ *Note:* Not all treatment plants will include all of the processes shown in
Figure 4.1. Specific processes have been included to facilitate discussion of
major potential problems with each process and its operation; this is information that may be important to the wastewater operator.

4.2 SCREENING

Preliminary treatment begins with *screening.* Screens remove large solids
such as rags, sticks, plastics, and similar materials from the wastewater.

109

110

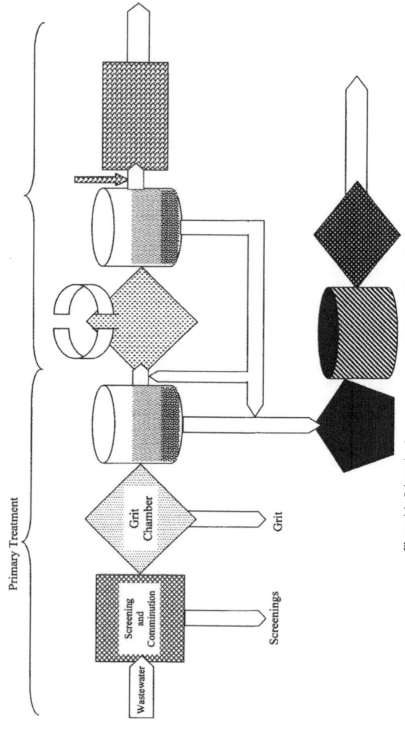

Figure 4.1. Schematic of wastewater treatment facility providing preliminary treatment.

✓ *Note:* Typically, a treatment plant will remove anywhere from 0.5 to 12 ft³ of screenings for each million gallons of influent received. This is equivalent to 3.5 to 80 m³ of screenings for each million cubic meters of wastewater received.

A typical *bar screen* is shown in Figure 4.2. It consists of a series of parallel bars or a perforated screen placed in a channel. The flow passes through the screen and the large solids are trapped on the bars for removal. The bar screen may be coarse (2–4 inch openings) or fine (0.75 to 2.0 inch openings). The bar screen may be manually cleaned (bars or screens are placed at an angle of 30° for easier solids removal—see Figure 4.2) or mechanically cleaned (bars are placed at 45° to 60° angle to improve mechanical cleaner operation).

The screening method employed (manual or mechanical) depends on the design of the plant, the amount of solids expected and whether the screen is for constant use or emergency use only. Manually cleaned screens are cleaned using a long tooth rake. Solids are manually pulled to the drain platform and allowed to drain before storage in a covered container. Mechanically cleaned screens use a rake assembly to collect the solids and move them out of the wastewater flow for discharge to a hopper. The screen may be continuously cleaned or cleaned on a time or flow controlled cycle.

Manual or mechanical cleaning is performed frequently enough to prevent solids buildup and reduce flow (water velocity) into the plant. The water velocity through the screen is important. A screen channel velocity of around 1.5 ft/s is recommended. If the velocity decreases below 1 ft/s or slower, grit will drop out of the flow and into the screening channel.

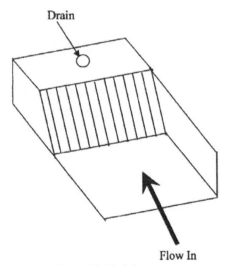

Figure 4.2. Basic bar screen.

✓ *Note:* If grit comes up with the screenings, the velocity in the screenings channel may be too slow. If multiple screenings channels are available, one of the channels could be taken out of service to flush the screen(s) and push the grit through.

To determine how many cubic feet of screenings were removed per million gallons of wastewater influent, the procedure described in Example 4.1 can be used.

Example 4.1

Problem:

The plant's screenings hopper is 4 ft wide and 6 ft long. Four days after the hopper was emptied the accumulated screenings were spread out evenly and measured to be 2 ft deep. The average daily plant flow rate over these four days (4 d) was 6.3 MGD (million gallons per day). How many cubic feet of screenings were removed per million gallons of wastewater influent?

Solution:

$$\frac{6.3 \text{ million gal}}{1\text{d}} \times 4\text{ d} = 25.2 \text{ million gal (MG)}$$

Removal per MG

$$\frac{4\text{ ft} \times 6\text{ ft} \times 2\text{ft}}{25.2 \text{ MG}} = \frac{1.90}{1\text{MG}} = 1.90 \text{ ft}^3/\text{MG}$$

As the availability of landfills continues to decrease, more attention will be given to the amount of water in the screenings. Generally speaking, screenings have a water content of about 80%. Screening units are often built with only a screenings hopper. A screenings hopper is not the ideal water drainage unit. Experience has shown that employment of a screening storage conveyor is more effective in removing water. Recent innovations have included screenings compactors to minimize water content. Some treatment facilities grind the screenings into small particles, which are then returned to the wastewater flow for removal in later processes.

✓ *Note:* Use caution, the screening area is the first location where the operator is exposed to wastewater flow. Any toxic, flammable or explosive gases present in the wastewater can be released at this point. Adequate ventilation must be provided. It is also important to remember that due to the grease attached to the screenings this area of the plant can be extremely slippery. Routine cleaning is required to minimize this problem.

4.3 SHREDDING

In some plants, shredding devices are installed after the bar screen or as alternatives to screening. Shredding devices reduce solids to a size that can enter the plant without causing mechanical problems or clogging.

Shredding processes include comminution and barminution devices.

The most common shredder is the *comminutor* (comminute means "cut up"). In this device all of the wastewater flow passes through the grinder assembly. The grinder consists of a screen or slotted basket, a rotating or oscillating cutter and a stationary cutter. Solids pass through the screen and are chopped or shredded between the two cutters. The comminutor will not remove solids that are too large to fit through the slots, and it will not remove floating objects. These materials must be removed manually.

Another device used in shredding is the *barminutor*. This device uses a bar screen to collect the solids which are then shredded and passed through the bar screen for removal at a later process. The barminutor is less frequently used due to higher maintenance requirements.

✓ *Note:* Use caution, only qualified maintenance operators should perform maintenance on shredding equipment.

4.4 GRIT REMOVAL

The purpose of *grit removal* is to remove the heavy inorganic solids, which could cause excessive mechanical wear. Grit includes sand, gravel, clay, egg shells, coffee grounds, metal filings, seeds, and other similar materials.

There are several devices or processes used for grit removal. All of the processes are based on the fact that grit is heavier than the organic solids that should be kept in suspension for subsequent treatment. Grit removal processes use gravity/velocity, aeration or centrifugal force to separate the solids from the wastewater.

4.4.1 GRAVITY/VELOCITY CONTROLLED GRIT REMOVAL

Gravity/velocity grit removal uses a channel or tank to reduce the velocity or speed of the wastewater to approximately 1 foot per second (fps). As long as the velocity is controlled in the range of 0.7 to 1.4 fps, the grit removal process will remain effective (see Figure 4.3). Gravity type systems may be manually or mechanically cleaned.

Velocity can be determined either by float and stopwatch or by flow and channel dimensions (see Equation 4.1).

$$\text{Velocity} = \frac{\text{Distance Traveled, feet}}{\text{Time Required, Seconds}} \qquad (4.1)$$

Example 4.2

Problem:

A float takes 25 seconds to travel 30 feet in a grit channel. What is the velocity of the channel?

Solution:

$$\text{Velocity} = \frac{30 \text{ feet}}{25 \text{ seconds}} = 1.2 \text{ fps}$$

Example 4.3

Velocity by flow and channel dimensions (see Equation 4.2).

$$\text{Velocity} = \frac{\text{Flow, MGD} \times 1.55 \text{ cfs/MGD}}{\text{\# Channels in Service} \times \text{Channel Width} \times \text{Water Depth}} \qquad (4.2)$$

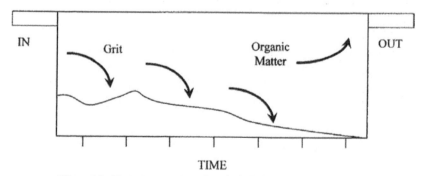

TIME

Figure 4.3. Illustrates operation of gravity/velocity grit removal process.

Problem:

The plant is currently using two grit channels. Each channel is 3 feet wide and has a water depth of 1.5 feet. What is the velocity when the influent flow rate is 3.2 MGD?

Solution:

$$\text{Velocity} = \frac{3.2\ \text{MGD} \times 1.55\ \text{cfs/MGD}}{2\ \text{channels} \times 3\ \text{ft} \times 1.5\ \text{ft}} = \frac{4.96\ \text{cfs}}{9\ \text{ft}^2} = 0.55\ \text{fps}$$

✓ *Note:* Since 0.55 is below the 0.7–1.4 level, the operator of this unit could consider taking one of the two channels out of service to increase velocity to the acceptable range.

4.4.2 AERATED SYSTEMS

Aerated grit removal systems use aeration to keep the lighter organic solids in suspension while allowing the heavier grit particles to settle out. Aerated grit removal systems may be manually or mechanically cleaned. The majority of the systems are mechanically cleaned.

4.4.3 CYCLONE DEGRITTER

The cyclone degritter uses a rapid spinning motion to separate the heavy inorganic solids or grit from the light organic solids and discharge them directly to a storage container. Inlet pressure is a critical control factor for the cyclone grit removal process.

4.5 KEY TERMS USED IN THIS CHAPTER

- *Bar screen*—coarse screen constructed of steel bars with clear openings not exceeding 2.5 in., normally used to protect wastewater lift pumps.
- *Comminutor*—a grinder that cuts solids that pass through a bar screen.
- *Grit chambers*—containers most commonly located after the bar racks and before the primary sedimentation tanks.
- *Screening*—first step in treating wastewater containing large solids.

- *Screenings*—rags, plastic, rocks, leaves, cans, and other debris retained on bar screens.
- *Shredder*—comminutor or barminutor used to shred waste solids that pass through a bar screen.

4.6 CHAPTER 4 SELF-TEST

4-1 What is the purpose of preliminary treatment?

4-2 What is the purpose of a bar screen?

4-3 What materials are often found in screenings?

4-4 What two ways are available for cleaning a bar screen?

4-5 What controls the velocity in a gravity type grit channel?

4-6 How many cubic feet of screenings will a plant remove from each million gallons of wastewater received?

4-7 What is the best velocity for the flow to go through a bar screen?

4-8 Below what velocity will grit settle in the screening channel?

4-9 What percentage of screenings is typically water?

4-10 Why is it important to remove grit from wastewater?

CHAPTER 5

Primary Sedimentation

Indecision is like a stepchild: If he does not wash his hands, he is called dirty, if he does, he is wasting water. (African Proverb)

5.1 PRIMARY TREATMENT

AFTER the pretreatment, the next step in the overall treatment process (see Figure 5.1) is to let the flow of wastewater slow down so that anything else that will settle by gravity can do so. This process is known as *primary sedimentation.*

5.2 SEDIMENTATION

The purpose of *sedimentation* is to remove settleable and floatable solids throughout the plant process. It is used in primary treatment, secondary treatment and advanced wastewater treatment processes.

5.2.1 SEDIMENTATION PROCESS

In a typical wastewater sedimentation process, wastewater enters a settling tank (primary clarifier) at a reduced velocity of approximately 1 foot per minute. Solids heavier than water settle to the bottom, while solids that are lighter than water float to the top (see Figure 5.2). Settled solids are removed as sludge, and floating solids are removed as scum. Wastewater leaves the sedimentation tank over an effluent weir to the next step of treatment. The efficiency or performance of the process is controlled by: detention time, temperature, tank design, and condition of the equipment.

117

118

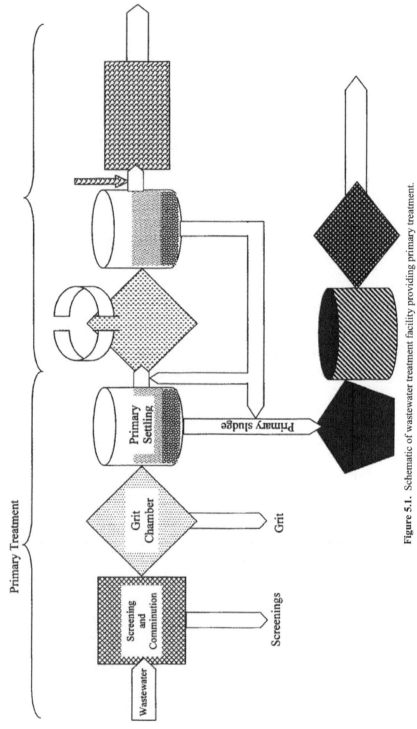

Figure 5.1. Schematic of wastewater treatment facility providing primary treatment.

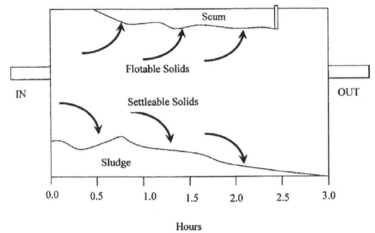

Figure 5.2. Sedimentation/flotation process.

5.2.2 SETTLING TANKS

The *settling tank* (or clarifier) optimizes the settling process. Sludge is removed from the tank for processing in other treatment unit processes. Flow enters the tank, is slowed and distributed evenly across the width and depth of the unit, passes through the unit and leaves over the effluent weir.

In primary treatment, detention time is between 1 to 3 hours (2 hours average).

5.3 PROCESS CONTROL CALCULATIONS

As with many other wastewater treatment plant unit processes, process control calculations aid in determining the performance of the sedimentation process. Process control calculations are used in the sedimentation process to determine:

- percent removal (see Chapter 2.14.1.12)
- hydraulic detention time (see Chapter 2.14.1.15)
- surface loading rate
- weir overflow rate
- sludge pumping
- percent total solids (% TS)

5.3.1 SURFACE LOADING RATE (SURFACE SETTLING RATE)

The *surface loading rate* is the number of gallons of wastewater passing over 1 square foot of tank per day. This can be used to compare actual conditions with design.

✓ *Note:* Plant designs generally use a surface loading rate of 300 to 1,200 gallons/day/ft .

$$\text{Surface Loading Rate} = \frac{\text{Flow, gal/day}}{\text{Settling Tank Area, ft}^2} \tag{5.1}$$

Example 5.1

Problem:

The settling tank is 120 feet in diameter and the flow to the unit is 4.5 MGD. What is the surface loading rate in gallons/day/ft²?

Solution:

$$\text{Surface Loading Rate} = \frac{4.5 \text{ MGD} \times 1,000,000 \text{ gal/MG}}{0.785 \times 120 \text{ ft} \times 120 \text{ ft}} = 398 \text{ gpd/ft}^2$$

5.3.2 WEIR OVERFLOW RATE (WEIR LOADING RATE)

The weir overflow rate is the amount of water leaving the settling tank per linear foot of weir. The results of this calculation can be compared with design. Normally weir overflow rates of 10,000 to 20,000 gal/day/ft are used in the design of a settling tank.

$$\text{Weir Overflow Rate} = \frac{\text{Flow, gal/day}}{\text{Weir Length, ft}} \tag{5.2}$$

Example 5.2

Problem:

The circular settling tank is 90 feet in diameter and has a weir along its circumference. This effluent flow rate is 2.55 MGD. What is the weir overflow rate in gal/day/foot?

Solution:

$$\text{Weir Overflow} = \frac{2.55 \text{ MGD} \times 1,000,000 \text{ gal/MG}}{3.1416 \times 90 \text{ ft}} = 9,018 \text{ gal/day/ft}$$

5.3.3 SLUDGE PUMPING

For the plant operator, for process control purposes, knowing the amount of sludge pumped each day is important. This information is not only important for proper operation of the sedimentation process, but for sludge treatment processes as well. Such information includes accurate data regarding the quantity of solids and volatile solids removed from the sedimentation tank.

$$\text{Solids Pumped} = \text{pump rate} \times \text{pump time} \times 8.34 \text{ lb/gal} \times \% \text{ solids} \quad (5.3)$$

$$\text{Volatile Solids} =$$
$$\text{pump rate} \times \text{pump time} \times 8.34 \text{ lb/gal} \times \% \text{ solids} \times \% \text{ vol. materials} \quad (5.4)$$

Example 5.3

Problem:

The sludge pump operates 15 minutes per hour. The pump delivers 30 gallons/minute of sludge. Laboratory tests indicate that the sludge is 5.1% solids and 69% volatile matter. How many pounds of volatile matter are transferred from the settling tank to the digester?

Solution:

Data:

pump time	15 minutes/hour
pump rate	30 gpm
% solids	5.1%
% V.M.	69%

Volatile solids, lbs/day =
$$30 \text{ gpm} \times (15 \text{ min/hr} \times 24 \text{ hr/day}) \times 8.34 \text{ lb/gal} \times 0.051 \times 0.69$$
$$= 3,169 \text{ lb/day}$$

5.4 SEDIMENTATION: EXPECTED PERFORMANCE

Primary sedimentation clarifiers can be expected to remove:

- Settleable solids   90–95%
- Total Suspended Solids   40–60%
- BOD$_5$ 25–35%

✓ *Note:* Performance expectations for settling devices used in other areas of plant operation are normally expressed as overall unit performance rather than settling unit performance.

5.5 KEY TERMS USED IN THIS CHAPTER

- *Sedimentation*—the separation from water, by gravitational settling, of suspended particles that are heavier than water. The terms sedimentation and settling are used interchangeably.

5.6 CHAPTER 5 SELF-TEST

5-1 What is the purpose of sedimentation?

5-2 What is the main purpose of a primary clarifier?

5-3 What percentage of the total solids is removed by primary settling?

5-4 What is the BOD removal rate in primary settling?

5-5 What is the average detention time in a primary clarifier?

CHAPTER 6

Secondary Treatment Processes

If you put a spoonful of wine into a barrel of sewage, you get sewage. If you put a spoonful of sewage into a barrel of wine, you get sewage. (Schopenhauer, Law of Entropy)

6.1 SECONDARY TREATMENT

SECONDARY TREATMENT refers to those treatment processes that use biological processes to convert dissolved, suspended, and colloidal organic wastes to more stable solids, which can either be removed by settling or discharged to the environment without causing harm.

Secondary treatment is defined by the Clean Water Act as producing an effluent with no more than 30 mg/L BOD_5 and 30 mg/L total suspended solids.

✓ *Note:* The CWA also states that ponds and trickling filters will be included in the definition of secondary treatment even if they do not meet the effluent quality requirements continuously.

Most secondary treatment processes decompose solids aerobically producing carbon dioxide, stable solids and more organisms. Since solids are produced, all of the biological processes must include some form of solids removal (settling tank, filter, etc.).

Secondary treatment processes can be separated into two large categories: fixed film and suspended growth systems.

6.1.1 FIXED FILM SYSTEMS

Processes that use a biological biomass or slime attached to some form of media are known as fixed film systems. Wastewater passes over or around the media and the slime. When the wastewater and slime are in contact, the organisms remove and oxidize the organic solids. The media may be stone, redwood, synthetic materials or any other substance that's durable (capable of withstanding weather conditions for many years), provides a large area for slime growth while offering sufficient open space for ventilation, and is not toxic to the organisms in the biomass. Fixed film devices include trickling filters and rotating biological contactors (RBCs).

6.1.2 SUSPENDED GROWTH SYSTEMS

Suspended growth system processes use a biological growth that is mixed with the wastewater. The most typical suspended growth systems are the various modifications of the activated sludge process (see Chapter 7).

6.2 WASTEWATER TREATMENT PONDS

Wastewater treatment can be accomplished using ponds. They are an economical treatment method that can produce a highly purified effluent. The degree of treatment provided depends on the type and number of ponds used. Ponds can be used as the sole type of treatment or they can be used in conjunction with other forms of wastewater treatment—that is, other treatment processes followed by a pond or a pond followed by other treatment processes.

6.2.1 TYPES OF PONDS BASED ON LOCATION

Ponds can be classified (named) based on their location in the wastewater treatment process and the type of wastes they receive (see Figure 6.1).

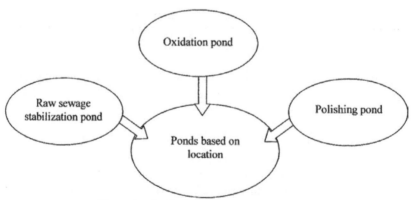

Figure 6.1. Ponds classification based on location.

6.2.1.1 Raw Sewage Stabilization Pond

Raw sewage stabilization ponds are the most common type of pond. This type of pond receives wastewater that has received no prior treatment (except screening or shredding; see Figure 6.2). Generally, this type of pond is designed to provide a minimum of 45 days detention time and to receive no more than 30 pounds of BOD_5 per day per acre. The quality of the discharge is dependent on the time of the year. Summer months produce high BOD_5 removals but low suspended solids removals. Winter months have poor BOD_5 removal but excellent suspended solids removals.

The pond consists of an influent structure, pond berm or walls and an effluent structure designed to permit selection of the best quality effluent. Normal operating depth of the pond is 3–5 feet. The process occurring in the pond involves bacteria decomposing the organics in the wastewater (aerobically and anaerobically) and algae using the products of the bacterial action to produce oxygen (photosynthesis; see Figure 6.3).

6.2.1.2 Oxidation Pond

An oxidation pond receives flows that have passed through a stabilization pond or primary settling tanks. This type of pond provides biological treatment, additional settling and some reduction in the number of fecal coliform present. An oxidation pond is normally designed using the same criteria as the stabilization pond.

6.2.1.3 Polishing Pond

A polishing pond receives flow from an oxidation pond or from other secondary treatment systems. Polishing ponds are designed to remove addi-

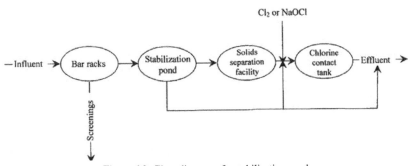

Figure 6.2. Flow diagram of a stabilization pond.

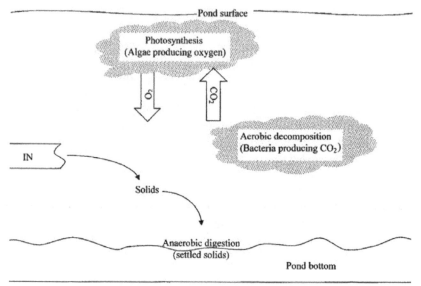

Figure 6.3. Stabilization pond process.

tional BOD_5, solids and fecal coliform and for some nutrient removal. Normal detention time is 1 to 3 days. Normal operating depth is 5 to 10 feet.

✓ *Note:* Excessive detention time or too shallow a depth will result in algae growth that increases effluent suspended solids concentrations.

6.2.2 TYPES OF PONDS BASED ON INTERNAL PROCESS

In addition to classification by location, ponds may be classified according to the type of processes occurring within the pond. These include the aerobic, anaerobic, facultative, and aerated processes (see Figure 6.4).

6.2.2.1 Aerobic Pond

In aerobic ponds, which are not widely used, oxygen is present throughout the pond. All biological activity is aerobic decomposition.

6.2.2.2 Anaerobic Pond

Anaerobic ponds are normally used to treat high-strength industrial wastes. No oxygen is present in the pond, and all biological activity is anaerobic decomposition.

6.2.2.3 Facultative Pond

The facultative pond is the most common type of pond (based on processes occurring). Oxygen is present in the upper portions of the pond, and aerobic processes are occurring. Absence of oxygen in the lower levels of the pond dictates the occurrence of anoxic or anaerobic processes only.

6.2.2.4 Aerated Pond

In an aerated pond, oxygen is provided through the use of mechanical or diffused air systems. When aeration is used, the depth of the pond and/or the acceptable loading levels may increase. Mechanical or diffused aeration systems may be used to supplement natural oxygen production or to replace it.

6.2.3 POND OPERATION

When compared with other wastewater treatment systems involving biological treatment, a pond treatment system is the simplest to operate and maintain.

Pond operation and maintenance activities include collecting and testing samples for dissolved oxygen and pH, removing weeds and other debris (scum) from the pond, mowing the berms, repairing erosion, and removing burrowing animals.

Dissolved oxygen and pH levels in the pond will vary throughout the day. Normal operation will result in very high dissolved oxygen and pH levels due to the natural processes occurring.

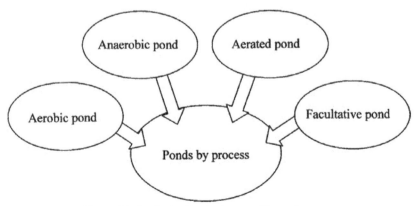

Figure 6.4. Ponds classification by type of internal process.

6.2.4 POND PROCESS CONTROL OPERATIONS

Wastewater operators and treatment managers use various process control operations to determine the state of operation (i.e., status) of the pond. These operations include determining pond area, pond volume, flow rate, hydraulic detention, hydraulic loading, population loading, and organic loading.

6.2.4.1 Pond Area in Acres

$$\text{Area, acres} = \frac{\text{Area, ft}^2}{43{,}560 \text{ ft}^2/\text{acre}} \qquad (6.1)$$

6.2.4.2 Pond Volume in Acre Feet

$$\text{Volume, acre-feet} = \frac{\text{Volume, ft}^3}{43{,}560 \text{ ft}^3/\text{acre-foot}} \qquad (6.2)$$

6.2.4.3 Flow Rate in Acre-feet/Day

$$\text{Flow, acre-ft/day} = \text{Flow, MGD} \times 3.069 \text{ acre-feet/MG} \qquad (6.3)$$

6.2.4.4 Flow Rate in Acre-Inches/day

$$\text{Flow, acre-in./day} = \text{Flow, MGD} \times 36.8 \text{ acre-inches/MG} \qquad (6.4)$$

6.2.4.5 Hydraulic Detention Time, days

$$\text{Hydraulic Det. Time} = \frac{\text{Pond vol., acre-ft}}{\text{Influent flow, acre-ft/day}} \qquad (6.5)$$

✓ *Note:* Normally in the range of 30–120 days.

6.2.4.6 Hydraulic Loading, inches/day

$$\text{Hydraulic Loading, in./Day} = \frac{\text{Influent flow, acre-inches/day}}{\text{Pond Area, Acres}} \qquad (6.6)$$

6.2.4.7 Population Loading

$$\text{Pop. Loading, People/Acre/Day} = \frac{\text{Population Served by System, People}}{\text{Pond Area, Acres}}$$

(6.7)

✓ *Note:* Normally in the range of 50–500 people per acre.

6.2.4.8 Organic Loading

Organic loading can be expressed as pounds of BOD_5 per acre per day (most common), pounds BOD_5 per acre-foot per day or people per acre per day.

$$\text{Organic Loading, lb } BOD_5/\text{Acre/Day} =$$
$$\frac{BOD_5, \text{mg/L} \times \text{Influent Flow, MGD} \times 8.34}{\text{Pond Area, Acres}}$$

(6.8)

6.3 TRICKLING FILTERS

In most wastewater treatment systems, the trickling filter follows primary treatment and includes a secondary settling tank or clarifier as shown in Figure 6.5. The process is a fixed film biological treatment method designed to remove BOD and suspended solids.

The trickling filter consists of several major components including distribution system, media, underdrains, effluent channel, secondary settling tank, and recirculation pumps and piping. Each of these components has one or more purposes.

In operation, wastewater is distributed evenly over the surface of the trickling filter media. As the wastewater flows over the surface of the media the organisms in the slime remove the organic matter from the flow (see Figures 6.6 and 6.7). The organisms aerobically decompose the solids producing more organisms and stable wastes, which either become part of the zoogleal slime or are discharged back into the wastewater flowing over the media. The wastewater continues through the filter to the underdrain system where it is collected and carried out of the filter. At the same time air flows through the filter (bottom to the top or top to bottom depending on temperature). Oxygen is transferred from the air to the wastewater and slime to maintain the aerobic conditions. Periodically the slime on the media becomes too heavy and portions will be released. This material known as *sloughings* is carried out of the filter with the wastewater flow and is removed in the settling tank following the filter.

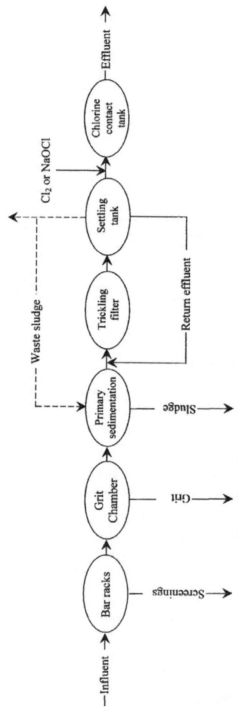

Figure 6.5. Simplified flow diagram of trickling filter used for wastewater treatment.

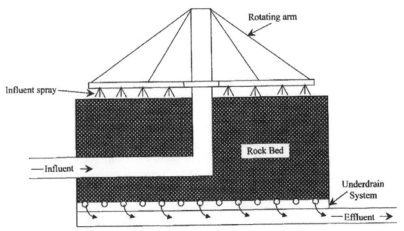

Figure 6.6. Schematic of cross-section of a trickling filter.

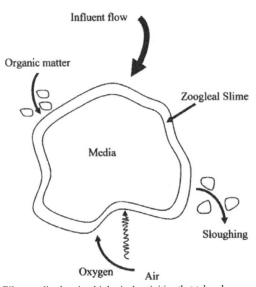

Figure 6.7. Filter media showing biological activities that take place on surface area.

6.3.1 TRICKLING FILTER RECIRCULATION

An important consideration in the operation of a trickling filter is that the microorganisms (the zoogleal slime) do not move. They just hang onto the media as slime waiting for the food to trickle by. To give the microorganisms another opportunity to eat food they missed, operators recycle clarified effluent. This is called *recirculation.*

Recirculation is used to reduce the organic loading, improve sloughing, reduce odors and reduce or eliminate filter fly or ponding problems. The amount of recirculation is dependent on the design of the treatment plant and the operational requirements of the process. Recirculation flow may be expressed as a specific flow rate (i.e., 2.5 MGD). In most cases, it is expressed as ratio (2:1, 0.5:1.0, etc.). The recirculation is always listed as the first number and the influent flow listed as the second number. Since the second number in the ratio is always 1.0, the ratio is sometimes written as a single number, namely the initial number, with the 1.0 being dropped.

Trickling filter flows can be recirculated from various points following the filter to various points before the filter (see Figure 6.8). The most common form of recirculation removes flow from the filter effluent or settling tank and returns it to the influent of the trickling filter.

6.3.2 TRICKLING FILTER PROCESS CONTROL CALCULATIONS

A number of calculations are useful in the operation of a trickling filter. For example, along with determining total flow, determining hydraulic loading and organic loading are also important. For the settling tank, calculating the detention time, surface settling rate, hydraulic loading, and the sludge pumping rate are important. With the exception of total flow, these parameters and their calculations are discussed in other sections of this manual. Thus, we have limited our discussion to trickling filter total flow calculation.

6.3.2.1 Trickling Filter Total Flow

If the recirculated flow rate is given, total flow is:

$$\text{Total Flow, MGD} = \text{Influent Flow, MGD} + \text{Recirc. Flow, MGD} \quad (6.9)$$

$$\text{Total Flow, gpd} = \text{Total Flow, MGD} \times 1,000,000 \text{ gal/MG} \quad (6.10)$$

The total flow to the trickling filter includes the influent flow and the recirculated flow. This can be determined using the recirculation ratio.

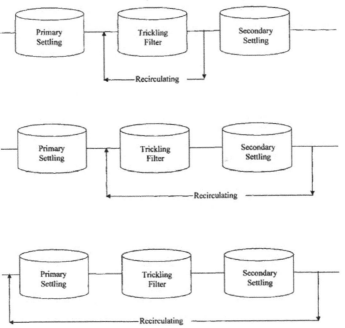

Figure 6.8. Trickling filter recirculation schemes.

Total Flow, MGD = Influent Flow × (Recirc. Rate + 1.0)   (6.11)

Example 6.1

Problem:

The trickling filter is currently operating with a recirculation rate of 1.5. What is the total flow applied to the filter when the influent flow rate is 4.25 MGD?

Solution:

Total Flow MGD = 4.25 MGD × (1.5 + 1.0) = 10.63 MGD

6.4 ROTATING BIOLOGICAL CONTACTORS (RBCs)

The *rotating biological contactor* (RBC) is a fixed film biological secondary treatment device. The basic process is similar to that occurring in the trickling filter.

In operation, a media, consisting of a series of circular disks mounted side by side on a common shaft is rotated through the wastewater flow (see Figure 6.9). The surface of the disk is covered with a biological slime similar to that on the media of a trickling filter. RBC units are usually installed in a concrete tank so that the surface of the wastewater passing through the tank almost reaches the shaft. This means that about 40% of the total surface area of the disks is always submerged. The shaft continually rotates at 1 to 2 rpm, and a layer of biological growth 2 to 4 mm thick is soon established on the wetted surface of each disk. The organisms in the slime assimilate (remove) organic matter from the wastewater for aerobic decomposition. The disk continues to rotate, leaving the wastewater and moving through the air. During this time, oxygen is transferred from the air to the slime. As the slime reenters the wastewater, excess solids and waste products are stripped off the media as sloughings. These sloughings are transported with the wastewater flow to a settling tank for removal.

Typically, a single contactor is not sufficient to achieve the desired level of treatment, so a group of contactors are used in series (see Figure 6.10). Each individual contactor is called a stage and the group is known as a train. Most RBC systems consist of two or more trains with three or more stages in each. One major advantage of the RBC system is the level of nitrification that can be achieved if sufficient stages are provided.

During operation, observations of the RBC movement, slime color, and appearance are helpful in determining system performance; that is, they can indicate process conditions. If the unit is covered, observations are usually limited

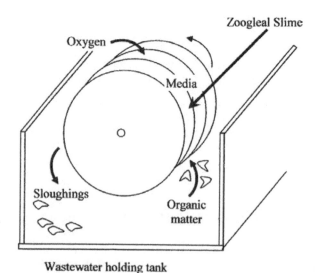

Wastewater holding tank

Figure 6.9. Rotating biological contactor (RBC) cross-section and treatment system.

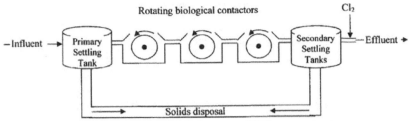

Figure 6.10. Rotating biological contactor (RBC) treatment system.

to that portion of the media that can be viewed through the access door. The following may be observed:

- Gray, shaggy slime growth—indicates normal operation
- Reddish brown, golden shaggy growth—nitrification
- White chalky appearance—high sulfur concentrations
- No slime—severe temperature or pH changes

In regard to typical performance, a well-maintained, properly operated RBC typically produces a high quality effluent: BOD @ 85–95% and Suspended Solids Removal @ 85–95%. The process may also reduce the levels of organic nitrogen and ammonia nitrogen significantly if designed for this purpose.

Advantages offered by RBCs:

(1) Short contact periods are required because of the large active surface.
(2) RBCs are capable of handling a wide range of flows.
(3) Sloughed biomass generally has good settling characteristics and can easily be separated from the waste stream.
(4) Operating costs are low because little skill is required in plant operation.
(5) Short retention time
(6) Low power requirements
(7) Elimination of the channeling to which conventional percolators are susceptible.
(8) Low sludge production and excellent process control.

Disadvantages of RBCs:

(1) Requirement for covering RBC units in northern climates to protect against freezing
(2) Shaft bearings and mechanical drive units require frequent maintenance.

6.5 KEY TERMS USED IN THIS CHAPTER

- *Recirculation*—used to reduce organic loading, improve sloughing, reduce odors and reduce or eliminate filter fly or ponding problems.
- *Secondary treatment stage*—of treatment whereby 85% of the organic matter in sewage is removed by making use of the bacteria in it.
- *Sloughings*—outer layers of zoogleal slime shed from an RBC.

6.6 CHAPTER 6 SELF-TEST

6-1 Give three classifications of ponds based upon their location in the treatment system.

6-2 Describe the processes occurring in a raw sewage stabilization pond (facultative).

6-3 What is the purpose of the polishing pond?

6-4 Name three main parts of the trickling filter and give the purpose or purposes of each part.

6-5 Why is the settling tank required following the trickling filter?

6-6 Describe the rotating biological contactor.

6-7 Describe the process occurring in the rotating biological contactor process.

6-8 What makes the RBC process similar to the trickling filter?

6-9 What makes the RBC perform at approximately the same levels of performance throughout the year?

6-10 The slime in the first stages of the RBC is gray and shaggy. The slime on the last two stages of the train is reddish brown. What does this indicate?

CHAPTER 7

Activated Sludge

Toilets in modern water closets rise up from the floor like white water lilies. The architect does all he can to make the body forget how paltry it is, and to make man ignore what happens to his intestinal wastes after the water from the tank flushes them down the drain. Even though the sewer pipelines reach far into our houses with their tentacles, they are carefully hidden from view, and we are happily ignorant of the invisible. (Milan Kundera)

7.1 BIOLOGICAL TREATMENT PROCESSES

To this point, the biological systems discussed included ponds, trickling filters, and rotating biological contactors (RBCs). These systems are effective unit processes in treating wastewater. However, trickling filters and RBCs are temperature sensitive, remove less BOD, and trickling filters cost more to build than activated sludge systems.

✓ *Note:* Although trickling filters and other treatment methods cost more to build than activated sludge systems, activated sludge systems are much more expensive to operate because of the need for energy to run pumps and blowers.

7.2 ACTIVATED SLUDGE PROCESS

Activated sludge refers to biological treatment processes that use a suspended growth of organisms to remove BOD and suspended solids. As shown in Figures 7.1 and 7.2, the process requires an aeration tank and a settling tank. In addition, support equipment (not shown in Figure 7.1) including return pumps, waste pumps, flow measurement devices for return and waste, as well as equipment to provide aeration (mixers and/or blowers), is also required.

139

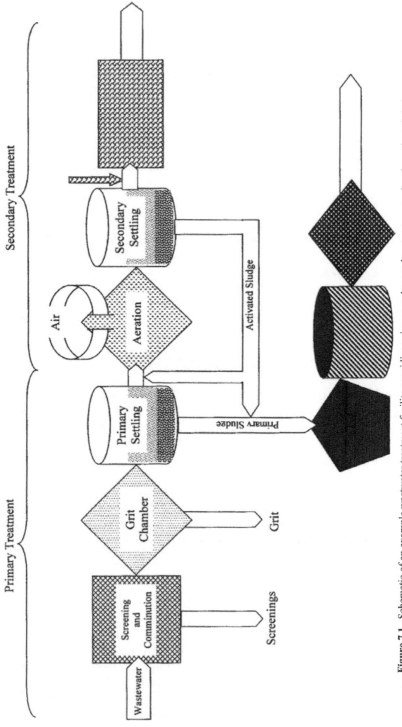

Figure 7.1. Schematic of an example wastwater treatment facility providing primary and secondary treatment using the activated sludge process.

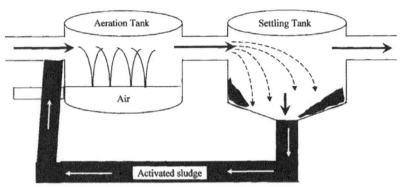

Figure 7.2. Secondary treatment—activated sludge process.

✓ *Note:* Activated sludge processes may or may not follow primary treatment. The need for primary treatment is determined by the process modification selected for use. As mentioned, all activated sludge systems include a settling tank following the aeration tank, as shown in Figure 7.1.

7.2.1 PROCESS DESCRIPTION

Primary effluent (or plant influent) is mixed with return activated sludge to form mixed liquor. The mixed liquor is aerated for a specified length of time. During the aeration the activated sludge organisms use the available organic matter as food, producing stable solids and more organisms. The suspended solids produced by the process and the additional organisms become part of the activated sludge. The solids are then separated from the wastewater in the settling tank. The solids are returned to the influent of the aeration tank (return activated sludge). Periodically the excess solids and organisms are removed from the system (waste activated sludge). Failure to remove waste solids will result in poor performance and loss of solids out of the system over the settling tank effluent weir.

7.2.2 FACTORS AFFECTING PROCESS PERFORMANCE

There are a number of factors that affect the performance of an activated sludge treatment system. These are listed as follows:

- temperature
- return rates
- amount of oxygen available
- amount of organic matter available

- pH
- waste rates
- aeration time
- wastewater toxicity

To obtain desired level of performance in an activated sludge system, a proper balance must be maintained between the amount of food (organic matter), organisms (activated sludge), and oxygen (dissolved oxygen).

7.3 ACTIVATED SLUDGE MODIFICATIONS

Many activated sludge process modifications exist. Each modification is designed to address specific conditions or problems. Such modifications are characterized by differences in mixing and flow patterns in the aeration basin, and in the manner in which the microorganisms are mixed with the incoming wastewater.

The major process modifications of the activated sludge process are: (1) conventional, (2) tapered aeration, (3) complete mix, (4) step aeration, (5) contact stabilization, (6) extended aeration, and (7) pure oxygen systems. Each of these modifications is described briefly in the following sections.

7.3.1 CONVENTIONAL MODIFICATION

This configuration requires primary treatment, and has the influent and returned sludge enter the tank at the head end of the basin; mixing is accomplished by the aeration system, and provides excellent treatment. On the downside, this modification requires large aeration tank capacity, higher construction costs, high initial oxygen demand, and is very sensitive to operation problems, such as bulking.

7.3.2 TAPERED AERATION

The tapered aeration system is similar to the conventional activated sludge process. The major difference is in the arrangement of the diffusers. The diffusers are close together at the influent end where more oxygen is needed. Toward the other end of the aeration basin, the spacing of the diffusers is increased.

7.3.3 STEP AERATION

In step aeration, the returned sludge is applied at several points in the aeration basin. Generally, the tank is subdivided into three or more parallel channels with around-the-end baffles, and the sludge is applied at separate channels or steps. The oxygen demand is uniformly distributed.

7.3.4 COMPLETE MIX AERATION

In complete mix aeration the influent and the returned sludge are mixed and applied at several points along the length and width of the basin. The contents are mixed, and the mixed liquor suspended solids (MLSS) flow across the tank to the effluent channel. The oxygen demand and organic loading are uniform along the entire length of the basin.

7.3.5 CONTACT STABILIZATION

In contact stabilization, primary treatment is not required. The activated sludge is mixed with influent in the contact tank where the organics are absorbed by microorganisms. The MLSS is settled in the clarifier. The returned sludge is aerated in the reaeration basin to stabilize the organics. The process requires approximately 50% less tank volume and can be prefabricated as a package plant for flows of 0.05 to 1.0 MGD. On the downside, this system is more complicated to control because many common control calculations do not work.

7.3.6 EXTENDED AERATION ACTIVATED SLUDGE

Extended aeration does not require primary treatment. It utilizes a large aeration basin where a high population of microorganisms is maintained. It is used for small flows from subdivisions, schools, etc. Prefabricated package plants utilize this process extensively. It has a channel in the shape of a race track, with rotors being used to supply oxygen and maintain circulation. Typically the process produces high-quality effluent and less activated sludge.

✓ *Note:* Oxidation ditch is a variation of extended aeration process.

7.3.7 PURE OXYGEN

Oxygen is diffused into covered aeration tanks. A portion of gas is wasted from the tank to reduce the concentration of carbon dioxide. The process is suitable for high-strength wastes where space may be limited. Special equipment for generation of oxygen is needed.

7.4 ACTIVATED SLUDGE PROCESS OPERATION

Operation of the activated sludge process requires more operator control than the other treatment processes discussed. The operator must adjust aeration, return rates and waste rates to maintain the balance of food, organisms and oxygen.

Operators must observe operation of the aeration basin to check on mixing pattern, type and amount of foam (normally small amounts of crisp white foam), color of activated sludge (normally dark, chocolate brown), and odors (normally musty or earth odor).

In regard to the settling tank, observations include flow pattern (normally uniform distribution), settling, amount and type of solids leaving with the process effluent (normally very clear).

In process control operations, sampling and testing are important. Testing may include settleability testing to determine the settled sludge volume; suspended solids testing to determine influent and mixed liquor suspended solids, return activated sludge solids, and waste activated sludge concentrations; determination of the volatile content of the mixed liquor suspended solids; dissolved oxygen and pH of the aeration tank; BOD and/or COD of the aeration tank influent and process effluent; and microscopic evaluation of the activated sludge to determine the predominant organism.

7.5 ACTIVATED SLUDGE PROCESS CONTROL CALCULATIONS

Activated sludge process control calculations may include determination of the thirty-and sixty-minute settled sludge volume (SSV_{30} and SSV_{60}), sludge volume index (SVI), and pounds of waste activated sludge removed from the process.

7.5.1 SETTLED SLUDGE VOLUME

$$SSV = \frac{\text{Settled Sludge Volume (SSV), mL} \times 1,000 \text{ mL/Liter}}{\text{Sample Volume, mL}} \quad (7.1)$$

Example 7.1

Problem:

A 2,000 mL sample of activated sludge is allowed to settle for thirty minutes. At the end of the settling time the sludge volume is 1,100 mL. What is the thirty-minute settled sludge volume (SSV_{30})?

Solution:

$$SSV_{30} = \frac{1,100 \text{ mL} \times 1,000}{2,000 \text{ mL}} = 550 \text{ mL/L}$$

7.5.2 SLUDGE VOLUME INDEX

Sludge volume index is a quality indicator. It reflects the settling quality of the sludge. As the SVI increases, the sludge settles slower, does not compact as well, and is likely to result in more effluent suspended solids.

$$SVI = \frac{\text{Settled Sludge Vol}_{30}, \text{mL/L} \times 1{,}000}{\text{Mixed Liquor Suspended Solids, mg/L}} \qquad (7.2)$$

Example 7.2

Problem:

The sample used in the example 7.1 has an MLSS concentration of 2,800 mg/L. What is the SVI?

Solution:

$$SVI = \frac{550 \text{ mL/L} \times 1{,}000}{2{,}800 \text{ mg/L}} = 196.43$$

7.5.3 WASTE ACTIVATED SLUDGE

Control of the activated sludge process requires accurate information on the quantity of solids removed from the process as waste activated sludge.

Waste, lb/day = WAS Conc., mg/L × WAS Flow, MGD × 8.34 lb/MG/mg/L

$$(7.3)$$

Example 7.3

Problem:

The operator wastes 0.44 MGD of activated sludge. The waste activated sludge has solids concentration of 5,840 mg/L. How many pounds of waste activated sludge are removed from the process?

Solution:

Waste, lb/day = 5,840 mg/L × 0.44 MGD × 8.34 = 21,430 lb/day

7.6 KEY TERMS USED IN THIS CHAPTER

- *Aeration*—air mixing that can be mechanical or diffused. Mechanical aeration systems use agitators or mixers to combine air and mixed liquor. Diffused aeration systems use pressurized air released through diffusers near the bottom of the tank.
- *Aeration tank*—a container designed to provide the required detention time and ensure that activated sludge and influent wastewater are thoroughly mixed. Tank design normally attempts to ensure no dead spots are created.
- *Bulking*—operational problem resulting from the presence of filamentous microorganisms or from entrained water in individual cells.
- *Return sludge*—settled activated sludge that is returned to the aeration basin to maintain the proper food-to-microorganism ratio.
- Settling tank—a tank designed to provide 2–4 hours hydraulic detention time.
- *Waste sludge*—activated sludge left over from the aeration basin or from the returned sludge line to the sludge-handling systems for treatment and disposal.

7.7 CHAPTER 7 SELF-TEST

7-1 What is the mixture of primary effluent and return sludge called?

7-2 What is the watery mixture of microorganisms and solids removed from the settling tank called?

7-3 What three things must be balanced to make the activated sludge process perform efficiently?

7-4 What are the two purposes of aeration?

7-5 List three observations the operator should make as part of the daily operation of the activated sludge process.

7-6 A 2,000 mL sample of activated sludge is allowed to settle for 60 minutes. At the end of the 60 minutes the sludge has settled to 1,200 mL. What is the SSV_{60} of the sample?

7-7 An activated sludge sample has a MLSS concentration of 2,350 mg/L. The SSV_{30} of the sample is 415 mL/L. What is the sludge volume index of the sample?

7-8 The operator wastes 0.069 MGD of activated sludge. The WAS concentration is 8,355 mg/L. How many pounds of activated sludge solids have been removed from the process?

7-9 Which activated sludge process aerates the return sludge before mixing it with the influent flow?

7-10 Activated sludge modification that is very sensitive to bulking: _____.

CHAPTER 8

Disinfection

The sewer is the conscience of the city. (Victor Hugo)

8.1 CONTROL OF WATERBORNE DISEASES

As mentioned, wastewater contains many types of human enteric organisms that are associated with various waterborne diseases. Typhoid, cholera, paratyphoid, and bacillary dysentery are caused by bacteria, and amebic dysentery is caused by protozoa. Common viral diseases include poliomyelitis and infectious hepatitis. Disinfection refers to selective destruction of disease-causing organisms in the water supply or in wastewater effluent.

✓ *Note:* The term *sterilization* denotes the complete destruction of all organisms. Pasteurization is selective destruction of undesired organisms by heat.

Wastewater, after secondary treatment to remove BOD and solids, may still contain large numbers of microorganisms. Some of these organisms may be pathogenic and may cause epidemics if discharged to receiving waters. Wastewater treatment must reduce the possibility of this happening. As with other steps of treatment, there are many processes available to achieve disinfection. The most widely used process is chlorination. Other processes include ultraviolet (UV) light, ozonation, and bromine chloride additions.

Chlorination of the water supply has been practiced since about 1850. Presently, chlorination of both water supply and wastewater effluent is an extremely widespread practice for the control of waterborne diseases. However, chlorination may result in the formation of chlorinated hydrocarbons, some of which are known to be carcinogenic. Therefore, either dechlorination or alternate methods of disinfection are used. Only the chlorination process is discussed in this text.

149

150

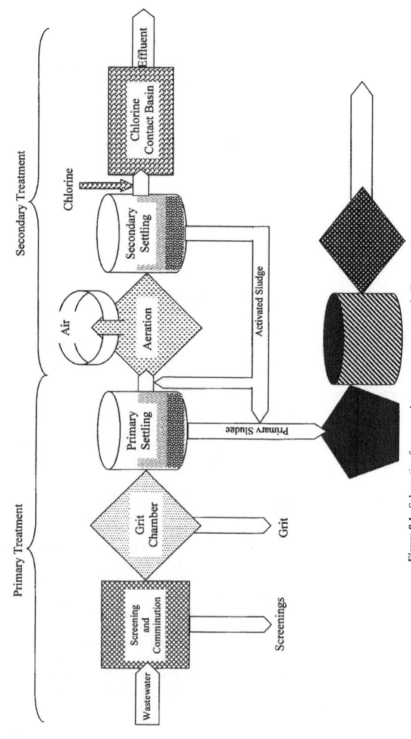

Figure 8.1. Schematic of an example wastewater treatment facility providing disinfection.

8.2 CHLORINATION FOR DISINFECTION

Chlorination, which follows all other steps of treatment (see Figure 8.1), reduces the population of organisms in the wastewater to levels low enough to ensure that pathogenic organisms will not be present in sufficient quantities to cause disease when the wastewater is discharged.

In use, chlorine is added to the wastewater to satisfy all chemical demands (such as sulfide, sulfite, ferrous iron, etc). When these initial chemical demands have been satisfied, chlorine will react with substances such as ammonia to produce chloramines and other substances which, although not as effective as chlorine, have disinfecting capability. This produces a combined residual that can be measured using residual chlorine test methods. If additional chlorine is added, free residual chlorine can be produced. Due to the chemicals typically found in wastewater, chlorine residuals are normally combined rather than free residuals. Control of the disinfection process is usually based on maintaining total residual chlorine of at least 1.0 mg/L for a contact time of at least 30 minutes at design flow.

Certain factors affect the disinfection process. These include residual level, contact time, and/or effluent quality. Failure to maintain the desired residual levels for the required contact time will result in lower efficiency and increased probability that disease organisms will be discharged.

8.3 CHLORINATION CHEMICALS

Chlorine used in the disinfection process normally is in the form of hypochlorite (similar to that used for home swimming pools) or free chlorine gas.

8.3.1 HYPOCHLORITE

Although there are some minor hazards associated with the use of hypochlorite (skin irritation, nose irritation, and burning eyes), it is relatively safe to work with. It is normally available in dry form as a white powder, pellet or tablet or in liquid form. It can be added directly using a dry chemical feeder or dissolved and fed as a solution.

The use of hypochlorite requires equipment for controlling its addition to wastewater. The specific equipment depends on the form of hypochlorite used. Liquid forms require the use of metering pumps capable of delivering varying flows of hypochlorite solution. Dry chemicals require the use of a feed system designed to provide variable does of the form used. The tablet form of hypochlorite requires the use of a tablet chlorinator designed specifically to provide the desired dose of chlorine. The hypochlorite solution or dry feed systems dispense the hypochlorite, which is then mixed with the flow. The treated wastewater then enters the contact tank to provide the required contact time.

8.3.2 ELEMENTAL CHLORINE

Elemental chlorine is a very hazardous substance, which can cause skin irritation, nausea, lung damage, and death, if inhaled in high concentrations. Chlorine is yellow-green in the gas form and amber colored in liquid form, it is 2.5 times heavier than air, non-flammable and a very strong oxidizing agent. It is available in different-sized containers (100, 150, and 1-ton containers or 50 and 90-ton railroad cars). The pressurized containers normally contain approximately 80% liquid chlorine and 20% gas. Although chlorine can be fed directly into the wastewater, most facilities dissolve the chlorine gas in water to reduce safety risks and facilitate movement to the point of application.

Due to the potential hazards associated with the use of chlorine the equipment requirements are significantly greater than those associated with hypochlorite use. The system most widely used is a solution feed system. In this system chlorine is removed from the container at a flow rate controlled by a variable orifice. Water moving through the chlorine injector creates a vacuum, which draws the chlorine gas to the injector and mixes it with the water. The chlorine gas reacts with the water to form hypochlorous acid and hydrochloric acid. The solution is then piped to the chlorine contact tank and dispersed into the wastewater through a diffuser.

Typically, larger facilities withdraw the liquid form of chlorine and use evaporators (heaters) to convert to the gas form. Small facilities normally draw the gas form of chlorine from the cylinder. As gas is withdrawn liquid will be converted to the gas form. This requires heat energy and may result in chlorine line freeze-up if the withdrawal rate exceeds available energy levels.

8.4 CHLORINATION OPERATION

In gaseous chlorine or hypochlorite-solution operations for disinfection or odor control, adjustment of feed rates is needed to ensure that required residual levels are maintained.

This normally requires chlorine residual testing and dosage adjustment based on the test results. Other activities include removal of accumulated solids from the contact tank, collection of bacteriological samples to evaluate process performance and maintenance of safety equipment (SCBA or air-line hose mask with escape bottle, safety lines, etc.).

Hypochlorite operation may also involve mixing the right solution (solution feed systems), adding powder or pellets to the dry chemical feeder or putting tablets in the tablet chlorinator.

Chlorination operations include adjustment of chlorinator feed rates, inspection of mechanical equipment, testing for leaks using ammonia swab (white smoke means leaks), changing containers (requires more than one person for safety), and adjusting the injector-water feed rate when required.

✓ *Note:* Use caution: elemental chlorine is an extremely toxic substance with potentially fatal hazards. For this reason the transport, storage and use of chlorine are regulated by many different State and Federal agencies. All persons required to work with chlorine should be trained in proper handling techniques and all procedures for storage, transport, handling and use of chlorine should be certified as complying with appropriate State and Federal regulations.

Chlorination operations require routine testing of total residual chlorine and may also require collection and analysis of samples to determine the fecal coliform concentration in the effluent.

8.4.1 PROCESS CONTROL CALCULATIONS

There are several calculations that are useful in operating a chlorination system. These include chlorine feed rate, chlorine dose, and chlorine demand.

8.4.1.1 Chlorine Feed Rate

$$\text{Feed Rate} = \text{Dose, mg/L} \times \text{Flow, MGD} \times 8.34 \text{ lb/MG/mg/L} \quad (8.1)$$

Example 8.1

Problem:

The chlorine dose is 7.25 mg/L and the flow rate is 3.25 MGD. What is the feed rate for chlorine in pounds per day?

Solution:

$$\text{Feed Rate} = 7.25 \text{ mg/L} \times 3.25 \text{ MGD} \times 8.34 = 197 \text{ lb/day}$$

8.4.1.2 Chlorine Dose

$$\text{Dose, mg/L} = \frac{\text{Feed Rate, lb/day}}{\text{Flow, MGD} \times 8.34 \text{ lbs/mg/L/MG}} \qquad (8.2)$$

Example 8.2

Problem:

The scale indicates that the plant has used 332 pounds of chlorine during the past twenty-four hours. The flow for the same period was 5.27 MGD. What is the dose of chlorine applied to the wastewater in milligrams/liter?

$$\text{Dose, mg/L} = \frac{332 \text{ pound/day}}{(5.27 \text{ MGD} \times 8.34 \text{ lbs/mg/L/MG})} = 7.6 \text{ mg/L}$$

8.4.1.3 Chlorine Demand

$$\text{Demand, mg/L} = \text{Dose, mg/L} - \text{Residual, mg/L} \qquad (8.3)$$

Example 8.3

Problem:

If the chlorine residual for the previous example was 1.3 mg/L, what was the chlorine demand?

$$\text{Demand, mg/L} = 7.6 \text{ mg/L} - 1.3 \text{ mg/L} = 6.3 \text{ mg/L}$$

8.5 KEY TERMS USED IN THIS CHAPTER

- *Chlorine*—strong oxidizing agent, which has strong disinfecting capability. A yellow-green gas, which is extremely corrosive, and is toxic to humans in extremely low concentrations in air.
- *Contact time*—length of time the disinfecting agent and the wastewater remain in contact.
- *Demand*—chemical reactions that must be satisfied before a residual or excess chemical will appear.
- *Disinfection*—removal of pathogenic organisms.
- *Dose*—amount of chemical being added in milligrams/liter.

- *Feed rate*—amount of chemical being added in pounds per day.
- *Residual*—amount of disinfecting chemical remaining after demand has been satisfied.
- *Sterilization*—removal of all living organisms.

8.6 CHAPTER 8 SELF-TEST

8-1 What is the difference between disinfection and sterilization?

8-2 The microorganisms that are disease carriers are called: _____.

8-3 The amount of chlorine that gets used up is called: _____.

8-4 To be effective enough chlorine must be added to satisfy the _____ and produce a _____ mg/L for at least _____ minutes at design flow rates.

8-5 Elemental chlorine is _____ in color, and is _____ times heavier than air.

8-6 Why must you take precautions when working with chlorine?

8-7 You are currently adding 387 pounds of chlorine per day to a wastewater flow of 5.8 MGD. What is the chlorine dose in mg/L?

8-8 The chlorine dose is 8.56 mg/L. If the residual is 1.08 mg/L the chlorine demand is _____.

8-9 Why are many facilities being required to install de-chlorination facilities following chlorination for disinfection?

Thought-provoking question:

8-10 The plant currently uses 48.3 pound of chlorine per day. Assuming the chlorine usage will increase by 10% during the next year, how many 1-ton cylinders of chlorine will be needed for the year (365 days)?

CHAPTER 9

Wastewater Solids Processing

Hector: Good-night, sweet Lord Menelaus.
Thersites: Sweet draught: 'sweet,' quoth a sweet sink, sweet sewer.
(William Shakespeare, Troilus and Cressida, Act V, Scene I)

9.1 WASTEWATER SOLIDS TREATMENT

IN the wastewater treatment process, solids (or process residuals) and biochemical oxygen demand (BOD) are removed from the waste stream before the liquid effluent is discharged to its receiving body. What remains to be disposed is a mixture of solids (sludge) containing large amounts of organic matter that, if discharged to the environment, would cause severe damage. Thus, these solids must be treated to ensure they can be disposed of (or beneficially reused) safely and economically.

In economic terms, the most costly and complex aspect of wastewater treatment can be the collection, processing, and disposal of solids residuals. The quantity of sludge (or biosolids) produced may be as high as 2% of the original volume of wastewater, depending somewhat on the treatment process being used. Because solids can contain as much as 97% water, and because the cost of disposal is related to the volume of sludge being processed, one of the primary purposes of solids treatment is to separate as much of the water from the solids as possible. Solids treatment methods are intended to accomplish this (see Figure 9.1).

9.2 PURPOSE OF SOLIDS TREATMENT

The purpose of solids treatment processes is multifaceted. For example, solids treatment processes are designed to:

- reduce organic content to permit safe disposal

157

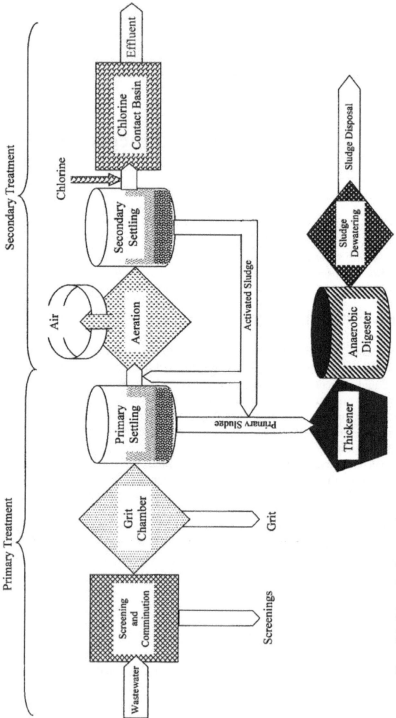

Figure 9.1. Schematic of an example wastewater treatment facility providing primary and secondary treatment using the activated sludge process.

- lessen moisture content to permit more economical treatment and/or disposal
- reduce pathogen content to safe levels for disposal
- produce a beneficial reuse product (biosolids)

9.3 SOLIDS TREATMENT METHODS

Solids treatment methods are generally divided into three major categories: thickening, stabilization, dewatering.

Thickening processes are designed to increase the solids content to permit more economical treatment. These include gravity thickeners, flotation thickeners, and solids concentrators.

Stabilization is designed to reduce volume and, at the same time, stabilize the organic matter to permit reuse or disposal. Stabilization methods include:

- aerobic digestion
- anaerobic digestion
- composting
- lime stabilization
- wet air oxidation (heat treatment)
- chemical oxidation (chlorine oxidation)
- incineration

Dewatering methods are designed to reduce volume to permit easy handling and economical reuse or disposal. Dewatering methods include:

- sand drying beds
- vacuum filters
- centrifuges
- filter presses (belt and plate)
- incineration

9.4 SOLIDS THICKENING

As mentioned, the purpose of solids thickening is to reduce process solids (residual) volume. Volume reduction is correlated to equipment and to the specific thickening process used. For example, equipment for gravity thickening (see section 9.4.1) consists of a thickening tank similar in design to the settling tank used in primary treatment. Generally the tank is circular and contains equipment for continuous solids collection. The collector mechanism uses heavier construction than that in a settling tank because the solids being moved are more concentrated. Pumping mechanisms with the gravity thickener (i.e., pump and flow measurement) allow withdrawal of thickened solids.

The flotation thickening process (see section 9.4.2) requires pressurized air, a vessel for mixing the air with all or part of the process residual flow, a tank for the flotation process to occur, solids collector mechanisms to remove the flat cake (solids) from the top of the tank and accumulated heavy solids from the bottom of the tank. Since the process normally requires chemicals to improve separation, it includes chemical mixing equipment, storage tanks, and metering equipment.

Solids concentrators (belt thickeners; see section 9.4.3) usually consist of a mixing tank, chemical storage and metering equipment and a moving porous belt.

9.4.1 GRAVITY THICKENING

As shown in Figure 9.1, solids withdrawn from primary treatment (and sometimes secondary treatment) are pumped to the thickener. The solids build-up in the thickener forms a solids blanket on the bottom. The weight of the blanket compresses the solids on the bottom and "squeezes" the water out. By adjusting the blanket thickness the percent solids in the underflow (solids withdrawn from the bottom of the thickener) can be increased or decreased. The clear water (*supernatant*) that rises to the surface is returned to the plant for treatment.

✓ *Note:* Gravity thickeners will normally produce 8–10% solids from primary underflow, 2–4% solids from waste activated sludge, 7–9% solids from trickling filter residuals and 4–9% solids from combined primary and secondary residuals.

9.4.2 FLOTATION THICKENING

Recycled water from the flotation thickener is aerated under pressure. During this time the water absorbs more air than it would under normal pressure. The recycle flow together with the chemical additives (if used) is mixed with flow. When the mixture enters the flotation thickener, the excess air is released in the form of fine bubbles. These bubbles become attached to the solids and lift them toward the surface. The accumulation of solids on the surface is called the float cake. As more solids are added to the bottom of the float cake it becomes thicker and water drains from the upper levels of the cake. The solids are then moved up an inclined plane by a scraper and discharged. The water below (subnatant) leaves the tank below the surface of the float solids and is recycled or returned to the plant for treatment.

✓ *Note:* In most cases, flotation thickeners are used to thicken biological process solids. Typical performance is 3–5% solids for waste activated sludge with polymer addition and 2–4% solids without polymer addition.

9.4.3 SOLIDS CONCENTRATORS

In the solids concentration process, the residual flow is chemically treated and then spread evenly over the surface of a porous belt. As the flow is carried down the belt (similar to a conveyor belt) the solids are mechanically turned or agitated and water drains through the belt. Currently this process is being used at several facilities where space limitations prevent the use of either gravity or flotation thickeners.

9.5 SOLIDS STABILIZATION

As mentioned, the purpose of solids stabilization is to stabilize the organic matter, reduce volume and eliminate pathogenic organisms. Solids stabilization processes include aerobic digestion, anaerobic digestion, composting, lime stabilization, thermal treatment (wet air oxidation), and chlorine oxidation.

The equipment required for solids stabilization depends on the specific process used. Equipment for aerobic digestion, for example, consists of an aeration tank similar in design to the aeration tank used for the activated sludge process. Either diffused or mechanical aeration equipment is necessary to maintain the aerobic conditions in the tank. Solids and supernatant removal equipment are also required.

Equipment for anaerobic digestion includes a sealed digestion tank with a fixed or floating cover, heating and mixing apparatus, gas storage tanks, solids and supernatant withdrawal devices and safety equipment.

Equipment for composting, chlorine oxidation, wet air oxidation (heat treatment) and lime stabilization is dependent on the process manufacturer and the specific process designer.

Performance of the stabilization processes varies with the type of process used. Generally, stabilization processes can produce 40% to 60% reduction of both volatile matter (organic content) and moisture.

9.5.1 AEROBIC DIGESTION

In aerobic digestion, process residuals are added to the digester and aerated to maintain a dissolved oxygen concentration of 1.0 mg/L. The aeration also ensures that the tank contents are well mixed. Generally, aeration continues for 20 days retention time. Periodically, aeration is stopped, and the solids are allowed to settle. The clear liquid supernatant is removed to provide more room in the digester. When no additional volume is available, solids are withdrawn for disposal.

9.5.2 ANAEROBIC DIGESTION

In anaerobic digestion, process solids (thickened or unthickened) are pumped into a sealed digester. The organic matter digests anaerobically by a two-stage process. Sugars, starches and carbohydrates are converted to volatile acids, carbon dioxide and hydrogen sulfide. The volatile acids are then converted to methane gas. This operation can occur in a single tank (single stage) or in two tanks (two stage). In a single-stage system supernatant and/or digested solids must be removed whenever flow is added. In a two-stage operation solids and liquids from the first stage flow into the second stage each time fresh solids are added. Supernatant is withdrawn from the second stage to provide additional treatment space. Periodically, solids are withdrawn for dewatering and/or disposal. The methane gas produced in the process may be used for many plant activities.

9.5.3 COMPOSTING BIOSOLIDS

In a composting operation, dewatered solids (biosolids) are usually mixed with a bulking agent (e.g., wood chips) and stored until biological stabilization occurs. The composting mixture is ventilated during storage to provide sufficient oxygen for oxidation and to prevent odors. After the solids are stabilized, they are separated from the bulking agent. The composted solids are then stored for curing and applied to farmlands or in other beneficial uses.

9.5.4 LIME STABILIZATION

In the lime stabilization process, residuals are mixed with lime to achieve a pH of 12.0. This pH is maintained for at least 2 hours. The treatment solids can than be dewatered for disposal or be applied directly to land.

9.5.5 THERMAL TREATMENT

Thermal treatment (or wet air oxidation) subjects process residuals to high temperature and pressure in a closed reactor vessel. The high temperature and pressure rupture the cell walls of any organisms present in the solids and cause chemical oxidation of the organic matter. This process substantially improves dewatering and reduces the volume of material for disposal. It also produces a very high-strength waste, which must be returned to the wastewater treatment system.

9.5.6 CHLORINE OXIDATION

Chlorine oxidation takes place in a closed vessel. In this process, chlorine (100–1,000 mg/L) is mixed with a recycled solids flow. The recycled flow and process residual flow are mixed in a reactor. The solids and water are separated after leaving the reaction vessel. The water is returned to the wastewater treatment system, and the treated solids are dewatered for disposal.

9.6 SOLIDS DEWATERING

As mentioned, the purpose of solids dewatering is to reduce volume by removing water. The equipment required for dewatering depends on the specific process used. Solids dewatering unit processes include sand drying beds, vacuum filters, belt filters, plate and frame filters, centrifuges, and incinerators.

9.6.1 SAND DRYING BEDS

Sand drying beds include an inlet pipe, splash pad containment walls, a drying bed, (consisting of gravel base, underdrains and 8–12 inches of filter grade sand), and a system to return filtrate (water) for treatment. In some cases the sand beds are covered to provide protection from rain and snow.

In operation, solids are pumped to the sand bed and allowed to dry by first draining off excess water through the sand and then by evaporation. This is the simplest and cheapest method for dewatering sludge, although it requires a great deal of manpower to clean the sand.

9.6.2 VACUUM FILTER

The vacuum filter includes filter media (belt, cloth, or metal coils), media support (drum), vacuum system, chemical feed equipment and conveyor belts to transport the dewatered solids.

In operation, chemically treated solids are pumped to a vat or tank in which a rotating drum is submerged. As the drum rotates, a vacuum is applied to the drum. Solids collect on the media and are held there by the vacuum as the drum rotates out of the tank. The vacuum removes additional water from the captured solids. When solids reach the discharge zone the vacuum is released and the dewatered solids are discharged onto a conveyor belt for disposal. The media is then washed prior to returning to the start of the cycle.

9.6.3 BELT FILTER AND PLATE AND FRAME FILTER

The belt filter includes two or more porous belts, rollers, and related handling systems for chemical makeup and feed, and supernatant and solids collection and transport.

In operation, a coagulant (polymer) is mixed with the influent solids in the belt filter. The chemically treated solids are discharged between two moving belts. First, water drains from the solids by gravity. Then, as the two belts move between a series of rollers, pressure squeezes additional water out of the solids, which are then discharged onto a conveyor belt for transport to storage/ disposal.

The plate and frame filter consists of a support frame, filter plates covered with porous material, a hydraulic or mechanical mechanism for pressing the plates together, and related handling systems for chemical makeup and feed, and supernatant and solids collection and transport.

In the filter solids are pumped between plates. Pressure is applied to the plates and water is "squeezed" from the solids. At the end of the cycle the pressure is released and as the plates separate the solids drop onto a conveyor belt for transport to storage or disposal.

9.6.4 CENTRIFUGE

Centrifuge equipment is of various types, which are related to operations. In general, these operations require the centrifuge, pumping equipment for solids feed and centrate removal, chemical makeup and feed equipment, and support systems for removal of dewatered solids.

In operation, a centrifuge spins at a very high speed. The centrifugal force generated "throws" the solids out of the water. Chemically conditioned solids are pumped into the centrifuge and the spinning action forces the solids to the outer wall of the centrifuge. The supernatant (water) flows inside the unit to a discharge point. The solids held against the outer wall are scraped to a discharge point by an internal scroll moving slightly faster or slower than the centrifuge speed of rotation.

9.6.5 INCINERATION

Incineration produces the maximum solids and moisture reductions. The equipment required depends on whether the unit is a multiple hearth or fluid-bed incinerator. Generally the system will require a source of heat to reach ignition temperature, a solids-feed system, and ash handling equipment. The system must also include all required equipment to achieve compliance with air pollution control requirements.

In operation, solids are pumped or conveyed to an incinerator. The solids are dried and then ignited (burned). As they burn, the organic matter is converted to carbon dioxide and water vapor, and the inorganic matter is left behind as ash or "fixed" solids, which are collected for disposal.

9.7 SOLIDS HANDLING PROCESS CONTROL CALCULATIONS

Wastewater operators are often called upon to make various process control calculations related to solids handling operations. In this section we cover a few of these basic process control calculations.

9.7.1 ESTIMATING DAILY SLUDGE PRODUCTION

The calculation for estimation of the required sludge pumping rate provides a method to establish an initial pumping rate or to evaluate the adequacy of the current withdrawal rate.

$$\text{Est. Pump Rate} = \frac{(\text{Infl. TSS Conc.} - \text{Effl. TSS Conc.}) \times \text{Flow} \times 8.34}{\% \text{ Solids in Sludge} \times 8.34 \times 1{,}440 \text{ min/day}} \quad (9.1)$$

Example 9.1

Problem:

The sludge withdrawn from the primary settling tank contains 1.4% solids. The unit influent contains 275 mg/L TSS, and the effluent contains 130 mg/L TSS. If the influent flow rate is 5.40 MGD, what is the estimated sludge withdrawal rate in gallons per minute (assuming the pump operates continuously)?

Solution:

$$\text{Sludge Rate} = \frac{(275 \text{ mg/L} - 130 \text{ mg/L}) \times 5.40 \times 8.34}{0.014 \times 8.34 \times 1{,}440 \text{ min/day}} = 39 \text{ gpm}$$

9.7.2 VOLATILE SOLIDS LOADING

Volatile solids loading for the aerobic digester is expressed in pounds of volatile solids entering the digester per day per cubic foot of digester capacity.

$$\text{Volatile Solids Loading} = \frac{\text{Volatile Solids Added, lb/day}}{\text{Digester Volume, ft}^3} \qquad (9.2)$$

Example 9.2

Problem:

The aerobic digester is 25 ft in diameter and has an operating depth of 26 ft. The sludge added to the digester daily contains 1,450 lb of volatile solids. What is the volatile solids loading in pounds per day per cubic foot?

Solution:

$$\text{Volatile Solids Loading} = \frac{1,450 \text{ lb/day}}{0.785 \times 25 \text{ ft} \times 25 \text{ ft} \times 26 \text{ ft}} = 0.11 \text{ lb/dayft}^3$$

9.7.3 DIGESTION TIME, DAYS

Digestion time is the theoretical time the sludge remains in the aerobic digester.

$$\text{Digestion Time, Days} = \frac{\text{Digester Volume, gal}}{\text{Sludge Added, gpd}} \qquad (9.3)$$

Example 9.3

Problem:

Digester volume is 210,000 gal. Sludge is being added to the digester at the rate of 12,500 gpd. What is the digestion time in days?

Solution:

$$\text{Digestion Time, Day} = \frac{210,000 \text{ gal}}{12,500 \text{ gpd}} = 16.8 \text{ days}$$

9.7.4 PH ADJUSTMENT

Occasionally, the pH of the aerobic digester will fall below the levels required for good biological activity. When this occurs, the operator must perform a laboratory test to determine the amount of alkalinity required to raise the pH to the desired level. The results of the lab test must then be converted to the actual quantity of chemical (usually lime) required by the digester.

$$\text{Chem. Required} = \frac{\text{Chem. Used in Lab Test, mg}}{\text{Sample Volume, Liters}} \times \text{Dig Vol MG} \times 8.34 \qquad (9.4)$$

Example 9.4

Problem:

The lab reports that it took 220 mg of lime to increase pH of a 1-L sample of the aerobic digester contents to pH 7.3. The digester volume is 250,000 gal. How many pounds of lime will be required to increase the digester pH to 7.3?

Solution:

$$\text{Chemical Req., lb} = \frac{220 \text{ mg} \times 250,000 \text{ gal} \times 3.785 \text{ L/gal}}{1\text{L} \times 454 \text{ g/lb} \times 1,000 \text{ mg/g}} = 458 \text{ lb}$$

9.7.5 ANAEROBIC DIGESTER: REQUIRED SEED VOLUME IN GALLONS

$$\text{Seed Volume (Gallons)} = \text{Digester Volume} \times \% \text{ Seed} \qquad (9.5)$$

Example 9.5

Problem:

The new digester requires a 25% seed to achieve normal operation within the allotted time. If the digester volume is 255,000 gallons, how many gallons of seed material will be required?

Solution:

$$\text{Seed Volume} = 255,000 \times 0.25 = 63,750 \text{ gal}$$

9.7.6 ANAEROBIC DIGESTER: VOLATILE ACIDS-TO-ALKALINITY RATIO

The volatile acids-to-alkalinity ratio can be used to control operation of an anaerobic digester.

$$\text{Ratio} = \frac{\text{Volatile Acids Concentration}}{\text{Alkalinity Concentration}} \qquad (9.6)$$

Example 9.6

Problem:

The digester contains 230 mg/L volatile acids and 1,880 mg/L alkalinity. What is the volatile acids/alkalinity ratio?

Solution:

$$\text{Ratio} = \frac{230 \text{ mg/L}}{1,880 \text{ mg/L}} = 0.12$$

9.7.7 ESTIMATED GAS PRODUCTION IN CUBIC FEET/DAY

The rate of gas production is normally expressed as the volume of gas (ft^3) produced per pound of volatile matter destroyed. The total cubic feet of gas a digester will produce per day can be calculated by

Gas Prod. (ft^3) = Vol. Matter In, lb/day × Vol. Matter Red. × Prod. Rate
$$(9.7)$$

Example 9.7

Problem:

The digester receives 11,550 lb of volatile matter per day. Currently, the volatile matter reduction achieved by the digester is 53%. The rate of gas production is 11.2 ft^3 of gas per pound of volatile matter destroyed. What is the gas production rate per day?

Solution:

Gas Prod. = 11,550 lb/day × 0.53 × 11.2 ft^3/lb = 68,560 ft^3/day

9.8 KEY TERMS USED IN THIS CHAPTER

- *Stabilization*—process where biosolids are stabilized to reduce pathogens, eliminate offensive odors, and control putrefaction.
- *Thickening*—process where biosolids are thickened to concentrate solids and reduce volume.

9.9 CHAPTER 9 SELF-TEST

9-1 Name three devices used to thicken waste activated sludge.

9-2 Name three sludge stabilization processes.

9-3 Name three sludge dewatering devices.

9-4 What makes an incinerator a unique sludge treatment device?

9-5 The supernatant contains 325 mg/L volatile acids and 1,850 mg/L of alkalinity. What is the volatile alkalinity ratio?

9-6 Liquids produced during solids treatment must be _____.

9-7 The purpose(s) of sludge treatment is (are):

9-8 Define biosolids.

9-9 The quantity of sludge produced may be as high as ____% of the original volume of wastewater.

9-10 What is the purpose of sludge stabilization?

CHAPTER 10

Sampling, Testing, and Reporting

All colors take to water in blue. A red rose on a blue dress ploughs through the weave of the material like a boat. (Malcolm de Chazal)

10.1 DETERMINING THE OBJECTIVES OF SAMPLING

WHEN a wastewater treatment manager is planning a sampling study or a daily sampling protocol, it is important, before initiating the study, to determine the objectives of sampling. One important consideration is to determine whether sampling will be accomplished at a single point or at isolated points. Additionally, frequency of sampling must be determined. That is, will sampling be accomplished at hourly, daily, weekly, monthly, or even longer intervals? Whatever sampling frequency is chosen, the entire process will probably continue over a protracted period.

When the on-shift wastewater operator performs sampling, the decision-making requirements mentioned above have already been made: where the samples are to be taken has been determined; the frequency of sampling has been determined; and whether or not the sampling will continue over a protracted period. Often the duration of a sampling method is tied to how long a specific treatment process will be in operation.

In the normal performance of assigned duties, the wastewater operator is required to take and test samples with the goal of monitoring overall plant and process performance—to determine the effectiveness of treatment. Though there are only a few process control functions to be actually performed and only minimal analysis is required to monitor and report plant daily performance, the importance of sampling and testing in wastewater treatment operations cannot be overstated.

10.2 WASTEWATER SAMPLING

In wastewater sampling the first critical step is to obtain good, valid information by collecting a representative sample.

171

✓ *Note:* A representative sample is one that has the same chemical and/or biological composition as the wastewater it came from.

The second critical step in sampling is to follow a predetermined, understandable, user-friendly sampling protocol.

Though it is true that sample type and collection point must always be based on the test requirements and the information sought, it is also true that basic guidelines should be used for all sampling activities. Thus, the third critical step in sampling is to follow sampling rules. Standard sampling rules that should be followed anytime sampling is undertaken are listed in the following:

Sampling Rules:

- Samples must be collected from a well-mixed location.
- Sampling points must be clearly marked and easy to reach.
- Safety should always be considered when selecting a sampling point.
- Large, non-representative objects must be discarded.
- No deposits, growths or floating material should be included in the sample.
- All testing must be started as soon as possible after sample collection.
- Samples containing high concentrations of solids or large particles should be homogenized in a blender.
- Sample bottles and sample storage containers should be made of corrosion resistant material, have leak proof tops, and be capable of withstanding repeated refrigeration and cleaning after use.
- Each sampling location should have a designated storage container used only for samples from that location.
- Appropriate safety procedures should always be followed when collecting samples (rubber gloves, washing after sampling, remaining within guardrails, etc.).

10.2.1 Sampling Devices and Containers

The tools of the sampling trade for sampling performed by wastewater operators (and others) always include *sampling devices* and *containers*. It is important to ensure that sampling devices are corrosion resistant, easily cleaned, and capable of collecting desired samples safely and in accordance with test requirements. Whenever possible, one sampling device should be assigned to each sampling point. Sampling equipment must be cleaned on a regular basis to avoid contamination.

✓ *Note:* Some tests require special equipment to ensure the sample is representative. Dissolved oxygen and fecal coliform sampling require special equipment and/or procedures to prevent collection of non-representative samples.

Sample containers may be specified for a particular test. If no container is specified, borosilicate glass or plastic containers may be used. Sample containers should be clean and free of soap or chemical residues.

10.2.2 SAMPLE TYPES

There are two basic types of samples: grab samples and composite samples. The type of sample used depends on the specific test, the reason the sample is being collected, and the requirements in the plant discharge permit.

10.2.2.1 Grab Samples

A *grab sample* is a discrete sample collected at one time and one location. It is primarily used for any parameter whose concentration can change quickly (i.e., dissolved oxygen, pH, temperature, total chlorine residual). Grab samples are representative only of the conditions at the time of collection. In some instances (small plant, limited staffing), grab samples for permit-related effluent testing are acceptable.

As mentioned, grab samples must be used to determine pH, total residual chlorine, dissolved oxygen (D.O.) and also fecal coliform concentrations. However, grab samples may also be used for any test that does not specifically prohibit their use.

✓ *Note:* Before collecting samples for any test procedure, it is best to review the sampling requirements of the test.

10.2.2.2 Composite Samples

A *composite sample* consists of a series of individual grab samples taken at specified time intervals and in proportion to flow. The individual grab samples are mixed together in proportion to the flow rate at the time the sample was collected to form the composite sample. The composite sample represents the character of the wastewater over a period of time.

10.2.2.2.1 Composite Sampling Procedure

Because knowledge of the procedure used in processing composite samples is important (a basic requirement) to the wastewater operator, the actual procedure used is covered in this section.

Procedure:

- Determine the total amount of sample required for all tests to be performed on the composite sample (since too little sample destroys the accuracy of test results, be sure to allow sufficient sample volume for duplicates and repeats when needed).
- Determine the treatment system's average daily flow.

✓ *Note:* Average daily flow can be determined by using several months' data—which will provide a more representative value.

- Calculate a proportioning factor

$$\text{Proportioning Factor (PF)} = \frac{\text{Total Sample Volume Required, mL}}{\text{Number of Samples to be Calculated} \times \text{Average Daily Flow, MGD}} \quad (10.1)$$

✓ *Note:* Round the proportioning factor to the nearest 50 units (i.e., 50, 100, 150, etc.) to simplify calculation of the sample volume.

- Collect the individual samples in accordance with the schedule (once/hour, once/15 minutes, etc.).
- Determine flow rate at time the sample was collected.
- Calculate the specific amount to add to the composite container.

$$\text{Required Volume, mL} = \text{Flow}^T \times \text{PF} \quad (10.2)$$

$$T = \text{Time sample was collected}$$

- Mix the individual sample thoroughly, measure the required volume, and add to composite storage container.
- Refrigerate the composite sample throughout collection period.

Example 10.1

Problem:

The effluent testing will require 4,400 mL of sample. The average daily flow is 4.5 MGD. Using the flows given below calculate the amount of sample to be added at each of the times shown.

Time	Flow, MGD
8 A.M.	3.88 MGD
9 A.M.	4.10 MGD
10 A.M.	5.05 MGD
11 A.M.	5.25 MGD
12 Noon	3.80 MGD
1 P.M.	3.65 MGD
2 P.M.	3.20 MGD
3 P.M.	3.45 MGD
4 P.M.	4.10 MGD

Solution:

$$\text{Proportioning Factor (PF)} = \frac{4{,}400 \text{ mL}}{9 \text{ Samples} \times 4.5 \text{ MGD}}$$

$$= 109 \text{ (rounded down to 100)}$$

$$\text{Volume}_{8 \text{ A.M.}} = 3.88 \times 100 = 388 \ (400)$$
$$\text{Volume}_{9 \text{ A.M.}} = 4.10 \times 100 = 410 \ (410)$$
$$\text{Volume}_{10 \text{ A.M.}} = 5.05 \times 100 = 505 \ (500)$$
$$\text{Volume}_{11 \text{ A.M.}} = 5.25 \times 100 = 525 \ (530)$$
$$\text{Volume}_{12 \text{ Noon}} = 3.80 \times 100 = 380 \ (380)$$
$$\text{Volume}_{1 \text{ P.M.}} = 3.65 \times 100 = 365 \ (370)$$
$$\text{Volume}_{2 \text{ P.M.}} = 3.20 \times 100 = 320 \ (320)$$
$$\text{Volume}_{3 \text{ P.M.}} = 3.45 \times 100 = 345 \ (350)$$
$$\text{Volume}_{4 \text{ P.M.}} = 4.10 \times 100 = 410 \ (410)$$

10.2.3 SAMPLE PRESERVATION METHODS

Because samples can change very rapidly, some tests (e.g., pH, Temperature, Total Residual Chlorine, Dissolved Oxygen) must always be performed immediately (within 15 minutes of collection). Other tests may include methods for preservation of the sample. The preservation method and the maximum allowable holding time are listed in the federal regulations governing wastewater sampling and testing. See Federal Regulation (40 CFR 136) *Guidelines Establishing Test Procedures for the Analysis of Pollutants Under the Clean Water Act.*

10.3 WASTEWATER TESTING METHODS

It is important to point out that all wastewater sampling and testing must be performed in accordance with the federal regulations. Moreover, references used for sampling and testing must correspond to those listed in the most current federal regulation. For the majority of tests, the following references are cited:

- *Standard Methods For Examination of Water and Wastewater,* American Public Health Association-American Water Works Association-Water Pollution Control Federation, current ed. Bacteriological Testing Only.
- *Standard Methods For Examination of Water and Wastewater,* current ed., American Public Health Association, American Water Works Association-Water Environment Federation, Washington, D.C.
- *Methods for Chemical Analysis of Water and Wastes,* U.S. Environmental Protection Agency, Environmental Monitoring Systems Laboratory—Cincinnati (EMSL-CK), EPA-600/4-79-020. Revised March 1993 and 1979 (where applicable).
- *Annual Book of ASTM Standards, Section 11, Water and Environmental Technology,* American Society of Testing Materials (ASTM), Philadelphia, PA.

✓ *Note:* Only those test methods specifically cited in the federal regulations are approved methods. Other methods contained in the cited references can be used only if the facility receives a variance from the U.S. Environmental Protection Agency.

10.3.1 TEST METHODS

The following sections provide information on sampling and testing for conventional pollutants (pH, TRC, D.O., BOD_5 and TSS).

Do not attempt to perform any of these tests based upon the information contained in these sections. For detailed information on the various approved methods consult the appropriate reference listed in the Federal Regulations or your NPDES permit. For additional information on other training materials and hands on workshops on sampling and testing procedures, contact your State Department of Environmental Quality Regional Office.

10.3.1.1 pH Testing

The approved method of *pH testing* requires the use of a pH meter (electrometric method). Grab samples are taken and tested using standard buffer solutions. Selected buffers should have pH values that bracket the expected pH of samples and be at least 2 pH units apart (i.e., pH 4, 7, 10).

The equipment used in pH testing is listed below:

- Beakers—50–100 mL capacity
- pH meter—Readable to 0.1 pH units with or without automatic temperature compensation (ATC).
- pH electrodes—One glass and one calomel or one combination electrode
- Thermometer
- Magnetic Stirrer (optional)
- Stirring Bars (optional)

Procedure:

✓ *Note:* The test procedure provided by the manufacturer of the specific instrument used should always be followed.

In general, the procedures used will include the following steps:

(1) Turn on the meter, and allow it to warm up.
(2) Standardize first with the buffer closest to the expected pH of the sample (normally pH 7.0).
(3) Check meter using a second buffer that will bracket the expected pH of the sample (normally pH 9 or 10).

✓ *Note:* The current Standard Methods procedure for pH requires use of a three-buffer standardization procedure. This means that step 3 must be repeated using a third buffer (normally pH 4.0).

(4) Gently agitate the buffer or sample during the measurement.
(5) pH is recorded when meter reading is steady.
(6) Always rinse and blot the electrodes with a soft tissue when changing from one solution to another. *Note:* Do not rub the electrodes.
(7) Always use grab samples for pH determinations.
(8) Always rinse electrodes with laboratory grade water and place in tap water or pH 7.0 buffer solution.

10.3.1.2 Total Residual Chlorine Sampling and Analysis

Currently, federal regulations cite six approved methods for determination of total residual chlorine (TRC). These are:

- DPD-Spectrophotometric
- Titrimetric—Amperometric Direct
- Titrimetric—Iodometric Direct
- Titrimetric—Iodometric Back
  - Starch Iodine Endpoint—Iodine Titrant
  - Starch Iodine Endpoint—Iodate Titrant
  - Amperometric Endpoint
- DPD-FAS Titration
- Chlorine Electrode

All of these test procedures are approved methods and, unless prohibited by the plant's NPDES discharge permit, can be used for effluent testing. Based on current most popular method usage in the United States, discussion is limited to:

DPD-Spectrophotometric
DPD-FAS Titration
Titrimetric—Amperometric Direct

✓ *Note:* Treatment facilities required to meet "non-detectable" total residual chlorine limitations must use one of the test methods specified in the plant's NPDES discharge permit.

For information on any of the other approved methods, refer to the appropriate reference cited in the Federal Regulations.

10.3.1.2.1 DPD Spectrophotometric

DPD reacts with chlorine to form a red color. The intensity of the color is directly proportional to the amount of chlorine present. This color intensity is measured using a colorimeter or spectrophotometer. This meter reading can be converted to a chlorine concentration using a graph developed by measuring the color intensity produced by solutions with precisely known concentrations of chlorine. In some cases, spectrophotometers or colorimeters are equipped with scales that display chlorine concentrations directly. In these cases, there is no requirement to prepare a standard reference curve.

If the direct reading colorimeter is not used, chemicals that are required to be used include:

- Potassium dichromate solution 0.100N
- Potassium iodide crystals
- Standard ferrous ammonium sulfate solution 0.00282N
- Concentrated phosphoric acid

- Sulfuric acid solution (1+5)
- Barium diphenylamine sulfonate 0.1%

If an indicator is not used, a DPD indicator and phosphate buffer (DPD-prepared indicator – buffer + indicator together) are required.

In conducting the test, a direct readout colorimeter designed to meet the test specifications, or a spectrophotometer (wavelength of 515 nm and light path of at least 1 cm), or a filter photometer with a filter having maximum transmission in the wavelength range of 490 to 530 nm and a light path of at least 1 centimeter are required. In addition, for the direct readout colorimeter procedure, a sample test vial is required. When the direct readout colorimeter procedure is not used, the equipment required includes:

- 250 mL Erlenmeyer flask
- 10 mL measuring pipets
- 15 mL test tubes
- 1 mL pipets (graduated to 0.1 mL)
- Sample cuvettes with 1 centimeter light path

✓ *Note:* A cuvette is a small, often tubular laboratory vessel, typically made of glass.

Procedure:

✓ *Note:* For direct readout colorimeters, follow the procedure supplied by the manufacturer.

Standard Procedure Using Spectrophotometer or colorimeter:

(1) Prepare a standard curve for TRC concentrations from 0.05 to 4.0 mg/L—chlorine versus % Transmittance.

✓ *Note:* Instructions on how to prepare the TRC concentration curve or a standard curve are normally included in the spectrophotometer manufacturer's operating instructions.

(2) Calibrate colorimeter in accordance with the manufacturer's instructions using a laboratory-grade water blank.
(3) Add one prepared indicator packet (or table) of the appropriate size to match sample volume to a clean test tube or cuvette; or

- Pipet 0.5 mL phosphate buffer solution;
- Pipet 0.5 mL DPD indicator solution;
- Add 0.1 g KI crystals to a clean tube or cuvette.

(4) Add 10 mL of sample to the cuvette.

(5) Stopper the cuvette and swirl to mix the contents well.

(6) Let stand for 2 minutes.

(7) Verify the wavelength of the spectrophotometer or colorimeter and check and set the 0% T using the laboratory grade water blank.

(8) Place the cuvette in instrument, read %T and record reading.

(9) Determine mg/L TRC from standard curve.

✓ *Note:* Calculations are not required in this test because TRC, mg/L is read directly from the meter or from the graph.

10.3.1.2.2 DPD-FAS Titration

The amount of ferrous ammonium sulfate solution required to just remove the red color from a total residual chlorine sample that has been treated with DPD indicator can be used to determine the concentration of chlorine in the sample. This is known as a *titrimetric* test procedure.

- The chemicals used in the test procedure include the following:
- DPD prepared indicator (buffer and indicator together)
- potassium dichromate solution 0.100N
- potassium iodide crystals
- standard ferrous ammonium sulfate solution 0.00282N
- concentrated phosphoric acid
- sulfuric acid solution (1+5)
- barium diphenylamine sulfonate 0.1%

✓ *Note:* DPD indicator and/or phosphate buffer are not required if prepared indicator is used.

The equipment required for this test procedure includes the following:

- 250 mL graduated cylinder
- 5 mL measuring pipets
- 500 mL Erlenmeyer flask
- 50 mL buret (graduated to 0.1 mL)
- magnetic stirrer and stir bars

Procedure:

(1) Add the contents of a prepared indicator packet (or tablet) to the Erlenmeyer flask, or

  - Pipet 5 mL phosphate buffer solution into an Erlenmeyer flask;

- Pipet 5 mL DPD indicator solution into the flask;
- Add 1 g KI crystals to the flask.

(2) Add 100 mL of sample to the flask.

(3) Swirl the flask to mix contents.

(4) Let the flask stand for 2 minutes.

(5) Titrate with ferrous ammonium sulfate (FAS) until the red color first disappears.

(6) Record the amount of titrant.

The calculation required in this procedure is

$$TRC, mg/L = mL \text{ of FAS used} \tag{10.3}$$

10.3.1.2.3 Titrimetric—Amperometric Direct Titration

In this test procedure, phenylarsine oxide (PAO) is added to a treated sample to determine when the test reaction has been completed. The volume of PAO used can then be used to calculate the TRC.

The chemicals for this test include the following:

- phenylarsine oxide solution 0.00564N
- potassium dichromate solution 0.00564N
- potassium iodide solution 5%
- acetate buffer solution (pH 4.0)
- standard arsenite solution 0.1N

Equipment used includes the following:

- 250 mL graduated cylinder
- 5 mL measuring pipets
- Amperometric titrator

Procedure:

(1) Prepare amperometric titrator according to manufacturer.

(2) Add 200 mL sample.

(3) Place container on titrator stand and turn on mixer.

(4) Add 1 g KI crystals or 1 mL KI solution.

(5) Pipet 1 mL of pH 4 (acetate) buffer into the container.

(6) Titrate with 0.00564N PAO.

When conducting the test procedure, as the downscale endpoint is neared, slow the titrant addition to 0.1 mL increments and note titrant volume used after each increment. When no needle movement is noted, the endpoint has been reached. Subtract the final increment from the buret reading to determine the final titrant volume.

For this procedure, the only calculation normally required is

$$\text{TRC, mg/L} = \text{mL PAO used} \qquad (10.4)$$

10.3.1.2.4 Iodometric Direct Titration

In this test, phenylarsine oxide (PAO) is added to a treated sample to a starch endpoint (blue to clear). The results of the titration are used to calculate the TRC of the sample.

Chemicals used include the following:

- phenylarsine oxide solution 0.00564N
- potassium dichromate solution 0.00564N
- potassium iodide crystals
- Iodine solution 0.0282N
- acetate buffer solution (pH 4.0)
- standard arsenite solution 0.1N
- starch indicator

Equipment used includes the following:

- 250 mL graduated cylinder
- 5 mL measuring pipets
- 500 mL Erlenmeyer flask
- 5 mL volumetric pipet
- 10 mL buret (graduated to 0.01 mL)
- 25 mL buret (graduated to 0.1 mL)
- magnetic stirrer and stir bars

Procedure:

(1) Pipet 4 mL (acetate) buffer into an Erlenmeyer flask.
(2) Add 1 gram KI crystals to the flask.
(3) Add 200 mL, 500 mL or 1,000 mL of sample.
(4) Titrate with 0.00564N sodium thiosulfate or PAO to pale yellow color.
(5) Add 1–2 mL of starch solution.
(6) Chlorine titration until the blue color disappears
(7) Repeat Steps 1–3 and steps 5–6 with an appropriate volume of laborato-

ry grade water for a negative blank. If no blue appears at step 5, titrate to the first appearance blue color with 0.0282N iodine solution, then back titrate with sodium thiosulfate for a positive blank.

The calculations for this (and similar) procedures may be as simple as shown below:

$$\text{TRC, mg/L} = \text{mL PAO used} \qquad (10.5)$$

On the other hand, the calculations required to determine TRC using the iodometric direct titration method (and other methods) may be a bit more complicated as demonstrated by the following equations and examples.

10.3.1.2.4.1 Iodometric Direct Titration Method

$$\text{TRC, mg/L} = \frac{(\text{Tit. used for sample, mL} \pm \text{Tit. used for Blank}) \times \text{Tit. N} \times 35,450}{\text{Sample Volume, mL}}$$

$$(10.6)$$

✓ *Note:* A positive blank (+) is added to the titrant volume and a negative blank (−) is subtracted from the titrant volume.

Example 10.2

Problem:

Using the information provided, determine TRC, mg/L.

mL of Sample	300 mL
Titrant used for sample	2.8 mL
Titrant used for blank	+0.3 mL
Titrant Normality	0.00564N

Solution:

$$\text{TRC, mg/L} = \frac{(2.8 \text{ mL} + 0.3 \text{ mL}) \times 0.00564\text{N} \times 35,450}{300 \text{ mL}} = 2.1 \text{ mg/L}$$

10.3.1.2.4.2 Iodometric Back Titration using Iodine Titrant

$$\text{TRC, mg/L} = \frac{[\text{PAO Added, mL} - (5 \times \text{Tit. Used for Sample, mL}) \times 200}{\text{Sample Volume, mL}} \qquad (10.7)$$

Example 10.3

Problem:

Using the information provided, determine TRC, mg/L.

mL of Sample	220 m/L
PAO added	4.5 m/L
Titrant Used for Sample	0.5 mL

$$\text{TRC, mg/L} = \frac{[4.5 \text{ mL} - (5 \times 0.5 \text{ mL})] \times 200}{220 \text{ mL}} = 1.8 \text{ mg/L}$$

Solution:

✓ *Note:* If the Normality (N) of the titrant used for the sample is not exactly 0.0282 N, a corrective factor must be applied to the equation. The correction factor is computed by dividing the actual normality of the iodine solution by 0.0282N.

$$\text{CF} = \frac{\text{Iodine Solution Normality}}{0.0282\text{N}} \qquad (10.8)$$

When a correction factor is required, the equation is modified as shown below.

TRC, mg/L =

$$\frac{[\text{PAO Added, mL} - (5 \times \text{Tit. Used for Sample} \times \text{Corr. Factor})] \times 200}{\text{Sample Volume, mL}}$$

$$(10.9)$$

Example 10.4

Problem:

Using the information provided below, determine TRC, mg/L.

mL of Sample	200 mL
PAO Added	4.0 mL
Titrant Used for Sample	0.5 mL
Correction Factor	0.95

Solution:

$$\text{TRC, mg/L} = \frac{[4 \text{ mL} - (5 \times 0.5 \text{ mL} \times 0.95)] \times 200}{200 \text{ mL}}$$

10.3.1.2.4.3 Iodometric Back Titration using Iodate Titrant

TRC, mL =

$$\frac{(\text{Iodate Added to Blank, mL} - \text{Iodate Added to Sample, mL}) \times 200}{\text{Sample Volume, mL}}$$

(10.10)

Example 10.5

Problem:

Using the information provided below, determine TRC, mL:

Ml of Sample	200 mL
Iodate Used for Blank	9.3 mL
Iodate Used for Sample	7.0 mL

Solution:

$$\text{TRC, mL} = \frac{(9.3 \text{ mL} - 7.0 \text{ mL}) \times 200}{200 \text{ mL}} = 2.3 \text{ mL}$$

10.3.1.3 Dissolved Oxygen Testing

As the name implies, the dissolved oxygen test (DO) is the testing procedure used to determine the amount of oxygen dissolved in samples of wastewater. The analysis for DO is a key test in water pollution control activities and waste treatment process control. There are various types of tests that can be run to obtain the amount of DO. In the following, we discuss two (of several) approved methods: (1) dissolved oxygen meter method and (2) azide modification of the Winkler Method.

10.3.1.3.1 Dissolved Oxygen Meter Method

If samples are to be collected for analysis in the laboratory, a special APHA sampler, or the equivalent, must be used. This is the case because, if the sample is exposed to or mixed with air during collection, test results can change dramatically. Therefore, the sampling device must allow collection of a sample that is not mixed with atmospheric air and allows for at least a 3× bottle overflow (see Figure 10.1).

Again, because the dissolved oxygen level in a sample can change quickly, only grab samples should be used for dissolved oxygen testing. Samples must be tested immediately (within 15 minutes) after collection.

✓ *Note:* Samples collected for analysis using the Modified Winkler Titration Method may be preserved for up to 8 hours by adding 0.7 mL of concentrated sulfuric acid or by adding all the chemicals required by the procedure. Samples collected from the aeration tank of the activated sludge process must be preserved using a solution of copper sulfate-sulfanic acid to inhibit biological activity.

The advantage of using the dissolved oxygen meter method is the meter can be used to determine dissolved oxygen concentration directly (see Figure 10.2). In the field, a direct reading can be obtained using a field probe (see Figure 10.3) or by collection of samples for testing in the laboratory using a laboratory probe (see Figure 10.4).

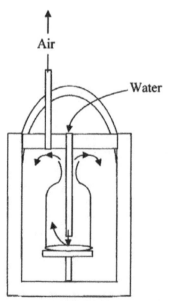

Figure 10.1. To prevent sample being collected from being mixed with air, the special device shown here is used. This device collects the sample below the surface and permits at least three overflows of the sample bottle.

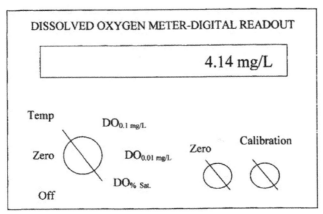

Figure 10.2. Dissolved oxygen meter.

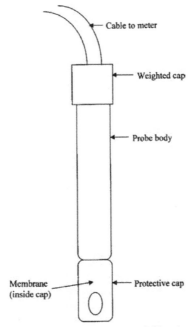

Figure 10.3. Dissolved oxygen-field probe.

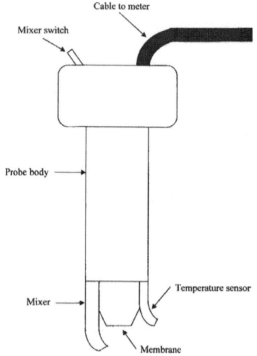

Figure 10.4. Dissolved oxygen-lab probe.

✓ *Note:* The field probe can be used for laboratory work by placing a stirrer in the bottom of the sample bottle, but the laboratory probe should never be used in any situation where the entire probe might be submerged.

The probe used in the determination of DO consists of two electrodes, a membrane and a membrane filling solution. Oxygen passes through the membrane into the filling solution and causes a change in the electrical current passing between the two electrodes. The change is measured and displayed as the concentration of dissolved oxygen. In order to be accurate, the probe membrane must be in proper operating condition and the meter must be calibrated prior to use.

The only chemical used in the dissolved oxygen meter method during normal operation is the electrode filling solution. However, in the Winkler DO method, chemicals are required for meter calibration.

Calibration prior to use is important. Both the meter and the probe must be calculated to ensure accurate results. The frequency of calibration is dependent on the frequency of use. For example, if the meter is used once a day, then calibration should be performed prior to use. There are three methods available for calibration: saturated water, saturated air, and the Winkler method. It is important to point out that if the Winkler method is not used as the routine calibration method, periodic checks using this method are recommended.

Procedure:

It is important to keep in mind that the meter and probe supplier's operating procedures should always be followed. Normally, the manufacturer's recommended procedure will include the following generalized steps:

(1) Turn DO meter on and allow 15 minutes for it to warm up.
(2) Turn meter switch to zero and adjust as needed.
(3) Calibrate meter using the saturated air, saturated water or Winkler azide procedure for calibration.
(4) Collect sample in 300 mL bottle or place field electrode directly in stream.
(5) Place laboratory electrode in BOD bottle without trapping air against membrane and turn on stirrer.
(6) Turn meter switch to temperature setting and measure temperature.
(7) Turn meter switch to DO mode and allow 10 seconds for meter reading to stabilize.
(8) Read DO mg/L from meter and record the results.

No calculation is necessary using this method because results are read directly from the meter.

10.3.1.3.2 Modified Winkler Method (Azide Modification)

In addition to the DO meter method, the *azide modification of the Winkler Method* can be used to test for DO content in wastewater samples. The azide modification method is best suited for relatively clean waters, because substances such as color, organics, suspended solids, sulfide, chlorine, and ferrous and ferric iron can interfere with the test results. If fresh azide is used, nitrite will not interfere with the test.

In operation, iodine is released in proportion to the amount of DO present in the sample. By using sodium thiosulfate with starch as the indicator, the sample can be titrated to determine the amount of dissolved oxygen present.

Chemicals used include:

- manganese sulfate solution
- alkaline azide—iodide solution
- sulfuric acid—concentrated
- starch indicator

- sodium thiosulfate solution 0.025N, or phenylarsine oxide solution 0.025N or potassium biniodate solution 0.025N
- Distilled or deionized water

Equipment used include:

- buret, graduated to 0.1 mL
- buret stand
- 300 mL BOD bottles
- 500 mL Erlenmeyer flasks
- 1.0 mL pipets with elongated tips
- pipet bulb
- 250 mL graduated cylinder
- laboratory grade water rinse bottle
- magnetic stirrer and stir bars (optional)

Procedure:

(1) Collect sample in a 300 mL BOD bottle.
(2) Add 1 mL manganous sulfate solution at the surface of the liquid.
(3) Add 1 mL alkaline-iodide-azide solution at the surface of the liquid.
(4) Stopper bottle and mix by inverting the bottle.
(5) Allow the floc to settle halfway in the bottle, remix and allow to settle again.
(6) Add 1 mL concentrated sulfuric acid at the surface of the liquid.
(7) Restopper bottle, rinse top with laboratory grade water and mix until precipitate is dissolved.
(8) The liquid in the bottle should appear clear and have an amber color.
(9) Measure 201 mL from the BOD bottle into an Erlenmeyer flask.
(10) Titrate with 0.025N PAO or thiosulfate to a pale yellow color, and note the amount of titrant.
(11) Add 1 Ml of starch indicator solution.
(12) Titrate until blue color first disappears.
(13) Record total amount of titrant.

10.3.1.3.2.1 Calculation

To calculate the dissolved oxygen concentration when the Modified Winkler Titration Method is used:

$$DO, mg/L = \frac{(Burett_{Final}, mL - Buret_{Start}, mL) \times N \times 8,000}{Sample\ Volume, mL} \quad (10.11)$$

✓ *Note:* Using a 200 mL sample and a 0.025 N (N = Normality of the solution used to titrate the sample) titrant reduces this calculation to

$$DO, mg/L = mL \text{ Titrant Used}$$

Example 10.6

Problem:

The operator titrates a 200 mL dissolved oxygen sample. The buret reading at the start of the titration was 0.0 mL. At the end of the titration the buret read 7.1 mL. The concentration of the titrating solution was 0.025 N. What is the DO concentration in mg/L?

$$DO, mg/L = \frac{(7.1 \text{ mL} - 0.0 \text{ mL}) \times 0.025N \times 8{,}000}{200 \text{ mL}} = 7.1 \text{ mg/L}$$

10.3.1.4 Biochemical Oxygen Demand Sampling and Analysis

The approved *biochemical oxygen demand sampling and analysis* procedure measures the DO depletion (biological oxidation of organic matter in the sample) over a five-day period under controlled conditions (20°C in the dark). The test is performed using a specified incubation time and temperature. Test results are used to determine plant loadings, plant efficiency and to determine compliance with NPDES effluent limitations. The duration of the test (5 days) makes it difficult to use the data effectively for process control.

The standard BOD test does not differentiate between oxygen used to oxidize organic matter and that used to oxidize organic and ammonia nitrogen to more stable forms. Since many biological treatment plants now control treatment processes to achieve oxidation of nitrogen compounds, there is a possibility that the BOD test for plant effluent and some process samples may produce test results based on both carbon and nitrogen oxidation. To avoid this situation a nitrification inhibitor can be added. When this is done, the test results are known as carbonaceous BOD (CBOD). A second uninhibited BOD test should also be run whenever CBOD is determined.

When taking a BOD sample, no special sampling container is required. Either a grab or composite sample can be used. BOD_5 samples can be preserved by refrigeration at or below 4°C (not frozen)—composite samples must be refrigerated during collection. Maximum holding time for preserved samples is 48 hours.

Using the incubation or dissolved approved test method, a sample is mixed with dilution water in several different concentrations (dilutions). The dilution water contains nutrients and materials to provide an optimum environment. The chemicals used are: dissolved oxygen, ferric chloride, magnesium sulfate, calcium chloride, phosphate buffer, and ammonium chloride.

✓ *Note:* Remember all chemicals can be dangerous if not used properly and in accordance with the recommended procedures. Review appropriate sections of the individual chemical materials safety data sheet (MSDS) to determine proper methods for handling and for safety precautions that should be taken.

Sometimes it is necessary to add (seed) healthy organisms to the sample. The dissolved oxygen of the dilutions and dilution water is determined. If seed material is used, a series of dilutions of seed material must also be prepared. The dilutions and dilution blanks are incubated in the dark for 5 days at 20°C ± 1°C. At the end of 5 days, the dissolved oxygen of each dilution and the dilution blanks is determined.

In order for the test results to be valid, certain criteria must be achieved. These test criteria are listed as follows:

- dilution water blank DO change must $\leq$ 0.2 mg/L
- initial DO must be > 7.0 mg/L but $\leq$ 9.0 mg/L (or saturation at 20°C and test elevation)
- sample dilution DO depletion must be $\geq$ 2.0 mg/L
- sample dilution residual DO must be $\geq$ 1.0 mg/L
- sample dilution initial DO must be $\geq$ 7.0 mg/L
- seed correction should be $\geq 0.6 \leq 1.0$ mg/L

The BOD_5 test procedure consists of 10 steps (for un-chlorinated water) as shown in Table 10.1. BOD_5 is calculated individually for all sample dilutions that meet the criteria. The reported result is the average of the BOD_5 of each valid sample dilution.

TABLE 10.1. BOD_5 Test Procedure.

1. Fill 2 BOD bottles with BOD dilution water; insert stoppers.
2. Place sample in 2 BOD bottles; fill with dilution water; insert stoppers.
3. Test for DO.
4. Incubate for 5 days.
5. Test for DO
6. Add 1 mL $MnSO_4$ below surface.
7. Add 1 mL alkaline KI below surface.
8. Add 1 mL H_2SO_4.
9. Transfer 203 mL to flask.
10. Titrate with PAO or thiosulfate.

10.3.1.4.1 BOD₅ Calculation (Unseeded)

Unlike the direct reading instrument used in the DO analysis, BOD results require calculation. There are several criteria used in selecting which BOD_5 dilutions should be used for calculating test results. Consult a laboratory testing reference manual (such as Standard Methods) for this information. At the present time there are two basic calculations for BOD_5. The first is used for samples that have not been seeded. The second must be used whenever BOD_5 samples are seeded. In this section we illustrate the calculation procedure for unseeded samples.

$$BOD_5 \text{ (Unseeded)} = \frac{(DO_{start}, \text{ mg/L} - DO_{final}, \text{ mg/L}) \times 300 \text{ mL}}{\text{Sample Volume, mL}} \qquad (10.12)$$

Example 10.7

Problem:

The BOD_5 test is completed. Bottle 1 of the test had a DO of 7.1 mg/L at the start of the test. After 5 days, bottle 1 had a DO of 2.9 mg/L. Bottle 1 contained 120 mL of sample.

Solution:

$$BOD_5 \text{ (Unseeded)} = \frac{(7.1 \text{ mg/L} - 2.9 \text{ mg/L}) \times 300 \text{ mL}}{120 \text{ mL}} = 10.5 \text{ mg/L}$$

10.3.1.4.2 BOD₅ (Seeded)

If the BOD_5 sample has been exposed to conditions that could reduce the number of healthy, active organisms, the sample must be seeded with organisms. Seeding requires use of a correction factor to remove the BOD_5 contribution of the seed material.

$$\text{Seed Correction} = \frac{\text{Seed Material } BOD_5 \times \text{Seed in Dilution, mL}}{300 \text{ mL}} \qquad (10.13)$$

$$BOD_5 \text{ (Seeded)} = \frac{[(DO_{start}, \text{ mg/L} - DO_{final}, \text{ mg/L}) - \text{Seed Corr.}] \times 300}{\text{Sample Volume, mL}}$$

$$(10.14)$$

Example 10.8

Problem:

Using the data provided below, determine the BOD$_5$.

BOD$_5$ of Seed Material		90 mg/L
Dilution #1	mL of seed material	3 mL
	mL of sample	100 mL
	Start DO	7.6 mg/L
	Final DO	2.7 mg/L

Solution:

$$\text{Seed Correction} = \frac{90 \text{ mg/L} \times 3 \text{ mL}}{300 \text{ mL}} = 0.90 \text{ mg/L}$$

$$\text{BOD}_5 \text{ (Seeded)} = \frac{[(7.6 \text{ mg/L} - 2.6 \text{ mg/L}) - 0.90] \times 300 \text{ mL}}{100 \text{ mL}} = 12 \text{ mg/L}$$

10.3.1.5 Solids Sampling and Testing

10.3.1.5.1 Total Suspended Solids

The term solid means any non-gaseous, non-liquid material suspended or dissolved in wastewater. Although normal domestic wastewater contains a very small amount of solids (usually less than 0.1%) most treatment processes are designed specifically to remove or convert solids to a form that can be removed or discharged without causing environmental harm.

When conducting solids testing, there are many things that affect the accuracy of the test or result in wide variations in results for a single sample. These include:

- Drying temperature
- Length of drying time
- Condition of desiccator and desiccant
- Non-representative samples lack of consistency in test procedure
- Failure to achieve constant weight prior to calculating results

There are several precautions that can help to increase the reliability of test results:

(1) Use extreme care when measuring samples, weighing materials and dry-ing or cooling samples.

(2) Check and regulate oven and furnace temperatures frequently to main-tain the desired range.

(3) Use an indicator drying agent in the desiccator that changes color when it is no longer good—change or regenerate the desiccant when necessary.

(4) Keep desiccator cover greased with the appropriate type of grease—this will seal the desiccator and prevent moisture from entering the desicca-tor as the test glassware cools.

(5) Check ceramic glassware for cracks and glass fiber filter for possible holes. A hole in a glass filter will cause solids to pass through and give inaccurate results.

(6) Follow manufacturer's recommendation for care and operation of analytical balances.

(7) Calibrate the drying oven or furnace temperature controller regularly.

In sampling for total suspended solids (TSS), samples may be either grab or composite and can be collected in either glass or plastic containers. TSS samples can be preserved by refrigeration at or below 4°C (not frozen). How-ever, composite samples must be refrigerated during collection. The maximum holding time for preserved samples is 7 days.

Test Procedure:

To conduct a TSS test, a well-mixed measured sample is poured into a filtration apparatus and, with the aid of a vacuum pump or aspirator, is drawn through a preweighed glass fiber filter. After filtration, the glass filter is dried at $104 \pm$ °C cooled and reweighed. The increase in weight of the filter and solids compared to the filter alone represents the total suspended solids.

An example of the specific test procedure used for total suspended solids is given below.

(1) Select a sample volume that will yield between 10 and 200 mg of residue with a filtration time of 10 minutes or less.

✓ *Note:* If filtration time exceeds 10 minutes, increase filter area or decrease volume to reduce filtration time.

✓ *Note:* For non-homogenous samples or samples with very high solids concentrations (i.e., raw wastewater or mixed liquor) use a larger filter to ensure a representative sample volume can be filtered.

(2) Place preweighed glass fiber filter on filtration assembly in a filter flask.

(3) Mix sample well and measure the selected volume of sample.

(4) Apply suction to filter flask and wet filter with a small amount of laboratory grade water to seat it.

(5) Pour the selected sample volume into filtration apparatus.

(6) Draw sample through filter.

(7) Rinse measuring device into filtration apparatus with three (3) successive 10 mL portions of laboratory grade water. Allow complete drainage between rinsings.

(8) Continue suction for three (3) minutes after filtration of final rinse is completed.

(9) Remove the glass filter from the filtration assembly (membrane filter funnel or clean Gooch crucible). If using the large disks and membrane filter assembly, transfer the glass filter to a support (aluminum pan or evaporating dish) for drying.

(10) Place the glass filter with solids and support (pan, dish or crucible) in a drying oven.

(11) Dry filter and solids to constant weight at 103–105°C (at least 1 hour).

(12) Cool to room temperature in a desiccator.

(13) Weigh the filter and support and record constant weight in test record.

10.3.1.5.1.1 TSS Calculations

To determine the total suspended solids concentration in mg/L we use the following equations:

- To determine weight of dry solids in grams

Dry Solids, grams =
$$\text{Wt. of Dry Solids and Filter, grams} - \text{Wt. of Dry Filter, grams} \tag{10.15}$$

- To determine weight of dry solids in milligrams (mg)

$$\text{Dry Solids, mg} = \text{Dry Solids, grams} \times 1{,}000 \text{ mg/gram} \tag{10.16}$$

- To determine the TSS concentration in mg/L

$$\text{TSS, mg/L} = \frac{\text{Dry Solids, mg} \times 1{,}000 \text{ mL/L}}{\text{mL sample}} \tag{10.17}$$

Example 10.9

Problem:

Using the data provided below, calculate total suspended solids (TSS):

Sample Volume, mL	250 mL
Weight of Dry Solids & Filter, grams	2.305 g
Weight of Dry Filter, grams	2.297 g

Solution:

$$\text{Dry Solids, grams} = 2.305 \text{ g} - 2.297 \text{ g} = 0.008 \text{ g}$$

$$\text{Dry Solids, mg} = 0.008 \text{ g} \times 1,000 \text{ mg/gram} = 8 \text{ mg}$$

$$\text{TSS, mg/L} = \frac{8.0 \text{ mg} \times 1,000 \text{ mL/L}}{250 \text{ mL}} = 32.0 \text{ mg/L}$$

10.3.1.5.2 Volatile Suspended Solids

When the total suspended solids are ignited at $550 \pm 50°C$, *the volatile (organic) suspended solids* of the sample are converted to water vapor and carbon dioxide and released to the atmosphere. The solids that remain after the ignition (ash) are the inorganic or fixed solids.

In addition to the equipment and supplies required for the total suspended solids test, you need the following:

- Muffle furnace ($550 \pm 50°C$)
- Ceramic dishes
- Furnace tongs
- Insulated gloves

Test Procedure:

(1) Place the weighed filter with solids and support from the total suspended solids test in the muffle furnace.
(2) Ignite filter, solids and support at $550 \pm 50°C$ for 15–20 minutes.
(3) Remove the ignited solids, filter and support from the furnace and partially air cool.
(4) Cool to room temperature in a desiccator.

(5) Weigh ignited solids, filter and support on an analytical balance.
(6) Record weight of ignited solids, filter and support.

10.3.1.5.2.1 Total Volatile Suspended Solids Calculations

To calculate total volatile suspended solids (TVSS) requires the following information:

- Weight of dry solids, filter and support in grams
- Weight of ignited solids, filter and support in grams

$$\text{Total Volatile Suspended Solids, mg/L} = \frac{(A-C)\times 1{,}000 \text{ mg/gram}\times 1{,}000 \text{ mL/L}}{\text{Sample Volume, milliliters}} \quad (10.18)$$

A = Weight of Dried Solids, Filter & Support
C = Weight of Ignited Solids, Filter & Support

Example 10.10

$$\text{Tot. Vol. Sus. Sol.} = \frac{(1.6530 \text{ g} - 1.6330)\times 1{,}000 \text{ mg/g}\times 1{,}000 \text{ mL}}{100 \text{ mL}}$$

$$= \frac{0.02\times 1{,}000{,}000 \text{ mg/L}}{100}$$

$$= 200 \text{ mL}$$

✓ *Note:* Fixed Suspended Solids (TFSS) is the difference between the volatile suspended solids (TVSS) and the total suspended solids (TSS) concentrations.

$$\text{Fixed Sus. Solids} = \text{Total Sus. Solids} - \text{Volatile Sus. Solids} \quad (10.19)$$

Example 10.11

Given:

Total Suspended Solids = 202 mg/L
Total Volatile Suspended Solids = 200 mg/L
Total Fixed Suspended Solids, mg/L = 242 mg/L – 200 mg/L = 42 mg/L

10.4 REPORTING

In general (requirements may vary depending upon State regulatory body with reporting authority), reporting must be made under the following conditions/situations:

- *Unusual or Extraordinary Discharge Reports*—must notify the Board by telephone within 24 hours of occurrence and submit written report within five (5) days. Report must include:

  (1) Description of the non-compliance and its cause.
  (2) Non-compliance date(s), time(s), and duration.
  (3) Steps planned/taken to reduce/eliminate.
  (4) Steps planned/taken to prevent reoccurrence.

- *Anticipated Non-Compliance*—Must notify the Board at least ten days in advance of any changes to the facility that may result in non-compliance.
- *Compliance Schedules*—Must report compliance or non-compliance with any requirements contained in compliance schedules no later than 14 days following scheduled date for completion of the requirement.
- *24-Hour Reporting*—Any non-compliance that can adversely affect State waters or may endanger public health must be reported orally within 24 hours of the time the permittee becomes aware of the condition. A written report must be submitted within five days.
- *Discharge Monitoring Reports (DMRs)*—Reports self-monitoring data generated during a specified period (normally 1 month). When completing the DMR, remember:

  — More frequent monitoring must be reported
  — All results must be used to complete reported values
  — Pollutants monitored by an approved method but not required by the permit must be reported
  — No empty blocks on the form should be left blank
  — Averages are arithmetic unless noted otherwise
  — Appropriate significant figures should be used
  — All bypasses and overflows must be reported
  — Report must be signed by the licensed operator
  — Report must be signed by responsible official
  — Department must receive by 10th of following month

10.4.1 SAMPLING AND TESTING

The general requirements of the permit specify minimum sampling and testing that must be performed on the plant discharge. Moreover, the permit will specify the frequency of sampling, sample type, and length of time for composite samples.

Unless a specific method is required by the permit, all sample preservation and analysis must be in compliance with the requirements set forth in the Federal Regulations *Guidelines Establishing Test Procedures for the Analysis of Pollutants Under the Clean Water Act* (40 CFR 136).

✓ *Note:* All samples and measurements must be representative of the nature and quantity of the discharge.

10.4.2 EFFLUENT LIMITATIONS

The permit sets numerical limitations on specific parameters contained in the plant discharge. Limits may be expressed as

- Average monthly quantity (KG/Day)
- Average monthly concentration (mg/L)
- Average weekly quantity (KG/Day)
- Average weekly concentration (mg/L)
- Daily quantity (KG/day)
- Daily concentration (mg/L)
- Hourly average concentration (mg/L)
- Instantaneous minimum concentration (mg/L)
- Instantaneous maximum concentration (mg/L)

10.4.3 COMPLIANCE SCHEDULES

If the facility requires additional construction or other modifications to fully comply with the final effluent limitations, the permit will contain a schedule of events to be completed to achieve full compliance.

10.4.4 SPECIAL CONDITIONS

Any special requirements or conditions set for approval of the discharge will be contained in this section. Special conditions may include:

- Monitoring required to determine effluent toxicity
- Pretreatment program requirements

10.4.5 LICENSED OPERATOR REQUIREMENTS

The permit will specify, based on the treatment system complexity and the volume of flow treated, the minimum license classification required to be the designated responsible charge operator.

10.4.6 CHLORINATION/DECHLORINATION REPORTING

Several reporting systems apply to chlorination alone or chlorination followed by dechlorination. It is best to review this section of the specific permit for guidance. If clarification is required, contact the appropriate State Regulatory Agency.

10.4.7 REPORTING CALCULATIONS

Failure to accurately calculate report data will result in violations of the permit. The basic calculations associated with completing the DMR are covered below.

10.4.7.1 Average Monthly Concentration

The average monthly concentration is the average of the

$$\text{AMC, mg/L} = \frac{\Sigma(\text{Test}_1 + \text{Test}_2 + \text{Test}_3 + \ldots + \text{Test}_n)}{N \text{ (Tests during month)}} \qquad (10.20)$$

10.4.7.2 Average Weekly Concentration (AWC)

The average weekly concentration (AWC) is the results of all the tests performed during a calendar week. A calendar week must start on Sunday and end on Saturday and be completely within the reporting month. A weekly average is not computed for any week that does not meet these criteria.

$$\text{AWC, mg/L} = \frac{\Sigma(\text{Test}_1 + \text{Test}_2 + \text{Test}_3 + \ldots + \text{Test}_n)}{N \text{ (tests during calendar week)}} \qquad (10.21)$$

10.4.7.3 Average Hourly Concentration

The average hourly concentration is the average of all the test results collected during a 60-minute period.

$$\text{AHC, mg/L} = \frac{\Sigma(\text{Test}_1 + \text{Test}_2 + \text{Test}_3 + \ldots + \text{Test}_n)}{N \text{ (tests during a 60 minute period)}} \qquad (10.22)$$

10.4.7.4 Daily Quantity (Kilograms/day)

Daily quantity is the quantity of a pollutant in kilograms per day discharged during a 24-hour period.

$$\text{Kilograms/Day} = \text{Concentration, mg/L} \times \text{Flow, MGD} \times 3.785 \text{ KG/MG/mg/L} \tag{10.23}$$

10.4.7.5 Average Monthly Quantity (AMQ)

Average monthly quantity (AMQ) is the average of all the individual daily quantities determined during the month.

$$\text{AMQ, KG/day} = \frac{\Sigma(DQ_1 + DQ_2 + DQ_3 + \ldots + DQ_n)}{N \text{ (tests during month)}} \tag{10.24}$$

10.4.7.6 Average Weekly Quantity

The average weekly quantity is the average of all the daily quantities determined during a calendar week. A calendar week must start on Sunday and end on Saturday and be completely within the reporting month. A weekly average is not computed for any week that does not meet these criteria.

$$\text{AWQ, KG/day} = \frac{\Sigma(DQ_1 + DQ_2 + DQ_3 + \ldots + DQ_n)}{N \text{ (tests during calendar week)}} \tag{10.25}$$

10.4.7.7 Minimum Concentration

The minimum concentration is the lowest instantaneous value recorded during the reporting period.

10.4.7.8 Maximum Concentration

Maximum concentration is the highest instantaneous value recorded during the reporting period.

10.4.7.9 Bacteriological Reporting

Bacteriological reporting is used for reporting fecal coliform test results. To make this calculation, the geometric mean is computed using the same selection criteria discussed for average weekly concentration and quantity calculations.

The easiest method used in making this calculation requires a calculator that can perform logarithmic (log) or Nth root functions.

$$\text{Geometric Mean} = \text{Antilog}\left[\frac{\log X_1 + \log X_2 + \log X_3 + \ldots + \log X_n}{N, \text{Number of Tests}}\right]$$

(10.26)

or

$$\text{Geometric Mean} = \sqrt[n]{X_1 \times X_2 \times \ldots \times X_n}$$

10.5 KEY TERMS USED IN THIS CHAPTER

- *Beaker*—container with an open top, vertical sides, and a pouring lip used for mixing chemicals.
- *Burette*—graduated glass tube fitted with a stopcock, used to dispense solutions during titration.
- *Composite sample*—a sample consisting of a series of individual grab samples taken at specified time intervals and in proportion to flow.
- *Dissolved oxygen (DO)*—oxygen dissolved in water, wastewater, or other liquid, usually expressed in milligrams per liter, parts per million, or percent of saturation.
- *Erlenmeyer flask*—bell-shaped container used for heating and mixing chemicals and culture media.
- *Iodometric method*—procedure for determining the concentration of dissolved oxygen in water, also known as the Winkler method.
- *Monitoring*—routine observation, sampling, and testing of water samples taken from different locations within a water system to determine water quality, efficiency of treatment processes, and compliance with regulations.
- *Representative sample*—a sample having the same chemical and/or biological composition as the wastewater it came from.
- *Titration*—method of analyzing the composition of a solution by adding known amounts of a standardized solution until a given reaction or end point (color change, precipitation, or conductivity change) is produced.

10.6 CHAPTER 10 SELF-TEST

10-1 How soon after the sample is collected must the pH be tested?

10-2 What is a grab sample?

10-3 Dissolved oxygen samples collected from the aeration tank and carried back to the lab for testing must be preserved by adding _____?

10-4 When is it necessary to use a grab sample?

10-5 If a grab sample is to be used to evaluate plant performance, when should the influent and effluent samples be collected?

10-6 What is a composite sample?

10-7 Why is a composite sample more representative of the average characteristics of the wastewater?

10-8 List three rules for sample collection.

10-9 The approved method for pH testing requires:

10-10 Who specifies the sample type, preservation method, and test method for effluent samples?

10-11 What is the maximum holding time and recommended preservation technique for BOD_5 samples?

10-12 The dissolved oxygen meter requires calibration at least once per
_____.

10-13 What is the difference between the BOD_5 and the $CBOD_5$ test?

10-14 Why is seeding required for samples with high or low pH or chlorinated samples?

10-15 What is the acceptable range of seed correction?

10-16 What is the acceptable preservation method for suspended solids samples?

10-17 Most solids test methods are based upon changes in weight. What can cause changes in weight during the testing procedure?

10-18 Who must sign the DMR?

CHAPTER 11

Comprehensive Review Exam

Now that you have reviewed each lesson and completed the chapter review questions, you may test your overall knowledge of the material contained in the text by completing the following review examination. For the questions you have difficulty answering or that you answer wrong, review the pertinent sections containing the applicable subject matter. Successful review and completion of all the requirements specified in this edition of the text should prepare you for licensure examinations.

Unlike the actual State licensure examinations, which contain an assortment of different types of questions (i.e., multiple choice, true or false, essay, completion questions, etc.), the final review examination presented here requires a written response to each question. We have formatted the examinations this way because experience has shown that when studying for an exam (any exam), it is always best to write out the "correct" answer (for retention purposes). Moreover, when studying for an exam, it is best to view only the correct answer instead of several different choices that might be confused as being the correct answer—which could enable the test taker to select the wrong answer on the licensure exam.

Upon completion of the review exam, check your answers with those given in Appendix B.

(1) Give three reasons for treating wastewater.

(2) Name two types of solids based on physical characteristics.

(3) Define organic.

(4) Name four types of microorganisms that may be present in wastewater.

(5) When organic matter is decomposed aerobically what materials are produced?

(6) Name three materials or pollutants that are not removed by the natural purification process.

(7) What are the used water and solids from a community that flow to a treatment plant called?

(8) Where do disease-causing bacteria in wastewater come from?

(9) What does the term pathogenic mean?

(10) What is wastewater called that comes from the household?

(11) What is wastewater called that comes from industrial complexes?

(12) The depth of water in the grit channel is 29 inches. What is the depth in feet?

(13) The operator withdraws 5,250 gallons of solids from the digester. How many pounds of solids have been removed?

(14) Sludge added to the digester causes a 1,920 cubic foot change in the volume of sludge in the digester. How many gallons of sludge have been added?

(15) The plant effluent contains 30 mg/L solids. The effluent flow rate is 3.40 MGD. How many pounds per day of solids are discharged?

(16) The plant effluent contains 25 mg/L BOD_5. The effluent flow rate is 7.25 MGD. How many kilograms per day of BOD_5 are being discharged?

(17) The operator wishes to remove 3,280 pounds per day of solids from the activated sludge process. The waste activated sludge concentration is 3,250 mg/L. What is the required flow rate in million gallons per day?

(18) The plant influent includes an industrial flow that contains 240 mg/L BOD. The industrial flow is 0.72 MGD. What is the population equivalent for the industrial contribution in people per day?

(19) The label of hypochlorite solution states that the specific gravity of the solution is 1.1288. What is the weight of 1 gallon of the hypochlorite solution?

(20) What is the purpose of the bar screen?

(21) What two methods are available for cleaning a bar screen?

(22) Name two ways to dispose of screenings.

(23) What is grit? Give three examples of material considered to be grit.

(24) The plant has three channels in service. Each channel is 2 feet wide and has a water depth of 3 feet. What is the velocity in the channel when the flow rate is 8.0 MGD?

(25) The grit from the aerated grit channel has a strong hydrogen sulfide odor upon standing in a storage container. What does this indicate and what action should be taken to correct the problem?

(26) What is the purpose of primary treatment?

(27) What is the purpose of the settling tank in the secondary or biological treatment process?

(28) The circular settling tank is 90 ft in diameter and has a depth of 12 feet. The effluent weir extends around the circumference of the tank. The flow rate 2.25 MGD. What is the detention time in hours, surface loading rate in gallons/day/ft^2 and weir overflow rate in gallons/day/foot?

(29) Give three classifications of ponds based upon their location in the treatment system.

(30) Describe the processes occurring in a raw sewage stabilization pond (facultative).

(31) How do changes in the seasons affect the quality of the discharge from a stabilization pond?

(32) What is the advantage of using mechanical or diffused aeration equipment to provide oxygen?

(33) Describe how the dissolved oxygen level of the pond changes during a day's time.

(34) What is the purpose of the polishing pond?

(35) Name three main parts of the trickling filter and give the purposes of each part.

(36) Name three classifications of trickling filters and identify the classification that produces the highest quality effluent.

(37) Describe the process occurring in the rotating biological contactor process.

(38) What makes the RBC process similar to the trickling filter?

(39) Describe the appearance of the slime when the RBC is operating properly. What happens if the RBC is exposed to a wastewater containing high amounts of sulfur?

(40) Microscopic examination reveals a predominance of rotifers. What process adjustment does this indicate is required?

(41) Increasing the wasting rate will _____ the MLSS, _____ the return concentration, _____ the MCRT, _____ the F/M ratio, and _____ the SVI.

(42) The plant adds 320 lb/day of dry hypochlorite powder to the plant effluent. The hypochlorite powder is 45% available chlorine. What is the chlorine feed rate in pounds per day?

(43) The plant uses liquid HTH, which is 67.9% available chlorine and has a specific gravity of 1.18. The required feed rate to comply with the plant's discharge permit total residual chlorine limit is 285 pounds/day. What is the required flow rate for HTH solution in gallons per day?

(44) The plant currently uses 45.8 pounds of chlorine per day. Assuming the chlorine usage will increase by 10% during the next year, how many 2,000 pound cylinders of chlorine will be needed for the year (365 days)?

(45) What is the difference between disinfection and sterilization?

(46) To be effective, chlorine must be added to satisfy the _____ and produce a _____ mg/L _____ for at least _____ minutes at design flow rates.

(47) Elemental chlorine gas is _____ in color, and is _____ times heavier than air.

(48) The sludge pump operates 30 minutes every three hours. The pump delivers 70 gpm. If the sludge is 5.1% solids and has a volatile matter content of 66%, how many pounds of volatile solids are removed from the settling tank each day?

(49) The aerobic digester has a volume of 63,000 gallons. The laboratory test indicates that 41 milligrams of lime were required to increase the pH of a 1-liter sample of digesting sludge from 6.0 to the desired 7.1. How many pounds of lime must be added to the digester to increase the pH of the unit to 7.4?

(50) Who must sign the DMR?

Answers to Chapter Self-Test Questions

Chapter 1:
Matching Exercise:

  (1) z
  (2) y
  (3) i
  (4) l
  (5) v
  (6) d
  (7) q
  (8) c
  (9) m
(10) n
(11) a
(12) j
(13) e
(14) k
(15) r
(16) u
(17) x
(18) h
(19) f
(20) g
(21) p
(22) w
(23) o
(24) s
(25) b
(26) t

Chapter 2:

2-1 13

2-2 363

2-3 6/9

2-4 5/8

2-5 9/14

2-6 1 5/12

2-7 5/8

2-8 0.75

2-9 0.0625

2-10 8.33, 7

2-11 1×10^7

2-12 250 gal, 3.78 L/gal = 945 liters

2-13 $A = L \times W$
    $= 9' \times 30'$
    $= 270 \text{ ft}^2$

2-14 $V = L \times W \times H$
    $= 25 \text{ ft} \times 60 \text{ ft} \times 8 \text{ ft}$
    $= 12{,}000 \text{ ft}^3$

2-15 $r = 35/2 = 17.5 \text{ ft}$
    $A = \pi = (3.14) \times 17.5^2 = 962 \text{ ft}^3$
    $V = \text{area} \times h$
    $= 962 \text{ ft}^3 \times 10 \text{ ft} = 9{,}620 \text{ ft}^3 \times 7.48 = 71{,}957.8 \text{ gal}$

2-16 $\text{Area} = \pi r^2$
    $r = 8/2 = 4''$
    $4'' = 4/12 = 1/3 \text{ ft}$
    $A = \pi r^2 = (\pi)(1/3)^2 = \pi(0.333)^2 = 0.348 \text{ ft}^2$
    $Q = V \times A = 4 \text{ ft/min} \times 0.348 \text{ ft}^2 = 1.39 \text{ ft}^3/\text{min}$
    $1.39 \text{ ft}^3/\text{min} \times 7.48 = 10.4 \text{ gal/min}$
    $10.4 \text{ gal/min} \times 60 = 624 \text{ gal/hr}$

2-17 $V = L \times \pi r^2$
    $= 12 \text{ ft} \times \pi(2.5 \text{ ft})^2$
    $= 12 \text{ ft} \times \pi(6.25 \text{ ft}^2) = 235.6 \text{ ft}$

2-18 $r = 25/2 = 12.5''$
$V = H \times \pi(12.5)^2$
$V = 44'' \times \pi(12.5)^2$
$V = 44'' \times 3.14 \times 156.3 \text{ in}^2 = 21,605.4 \text{ in}^3$

2-19 $73/100 = 0.73$, add to $1 = 1 + 0.73 = 1.73$
$1.73 \times 14,000 \text{ gal} = 24,220 \text{ gal}$

2-20 $50 \text{ gal}/1 \times 8.34 \text{ lb/gal} = 417 \text{ lb}$

2-21 $135 \text{ ft}^3/1 \times 62.4 \text{ lb/ft}^3 = 8,424 \text{ lb}$

2-22 $40 \text{ ft}/1 \times 0.433 \text{ psi}/1 \text{ ft} = 17.3 \text{ psi}$

2-23 $1.5 \text{ cfs}/1 \times 448 \text{ gpm}/1 \text{ cfs} = 672 \text{ gpm}$

2-24 $DT = 6,575 \text{ gal}/160 \text{ gal/min} = 41 \text{ minutes}$

2-25 $40''/12''/\text{ft} = 3.3 \text{ ft}$

2-26 $5450 \text{ gal} \times 8.34 \text{ lb/gal} = 45,453 \text{ lb}$

2-27 $38 \text{ mg/L} \times 3.89 \text{ MGD} \times 8.34 \text{ lb/MG/mg/L} = 1.233 \text{ lb/day}$

2-28 $26 \text{ mg/L} \times 7.25 \text{ MGD} \times 3.785 \text{ kg/mg/L} = 713 \text{ kg/day}$

2-29 $\dfrac{3,540 \text{ lb/day}}{3,524 \text{ mg/L} \times 8.34 \text{ lb/MG/L}} = 0.120 \text{ MG}$

2-30 8.5 lb/gal

2-31 $\dfrac{45 \text{ lb/cu ft}}{62.4 \text{ lb/cu ft}} = 0.7211 \text{ cu ft}$

2-32 $\dfrac{(30')(1,800 \text{ gpm})(8.34 \text{ lb/gal})}{33,000 \text{ ft-lb/min/hp}} = 13.6 \text{ hp}$

2-33 $\dfrac{0.785 \times 60' \times 60' \times 26' \times 7.48 \text{ gal/ft}^3}{5,200 \text{ gal/day}} = 106 \text{ DT days}$

Chapter 3:

3-1 Human and animal discharges—body discharges
Household wastes—garbage, paper, cleaning materials, etc.
Industrial wastes—waste materials from industrial processes
Stormwater runoff—large volume of water, sand and clay
Groundwater infiltration—large volume of water

3-2 bacteria, protozoa, rotifers, algae, viruses

3-3 pH, supply of organic matter, supply of oxygen, nutrients

3-4 Water from street drain, parking lots, roof drains, etc.
It can hydraulically overload the plant.

3-5 domestic, sanitary, industrial, stormwater, combined

3-6 pathogenic organisms

3-7 A measure of the amount of organic matter that can be used as food by the microorganisms. A measure of the strength of wastewater.

3-8 prevent disease, protect aquatic organisms, protect water quality

3-9 2,350 ft – 2,250 ft = 100 ft total static load

3-10 Q, cfs = 4 ft × (18 in/12 in/ft) × 1.3 fps = 7.8 cfs

$$Q, \text{MGD} = \frac{7.8 \text{ cfs}}{1.55 \text{ cfs/MGD}}$$

$$Q, \text{MGD} = 5 \text{ MGD}$$

Chapter 4:

4-1 To protect plant equipment and remove materials that are not affected by treatment.

4-2 To remove large solids

4-3 Include rags, rocks, plastics, leaves and branches

4-4 Manual/mechanical

4-5 Rate of flow, depth of the wastewater in the channel, width of the channel, and number of channels in service.

4-6 0.5 to 12 ft^3 of screenings per million gal of wastewater received.

4-7 1.5ft/sec

4-8 < 1 ft/sec

4-9 80%

4-10 Prevent excessive wear to pumps and to preserve valuable space in downstream processes.

Chapter 5:

5-1 To remove settleable and floatable solids

5-2 To remove settleable solids

5-3 90–95%

5-4 25–35%

5-5 1–3 hours (2 hr. average)

Chapter 6:

6-1 Stabilization, oxidation, polishing

6-2 As solids settle to the bottom and decompose anaerobically, dissolved and suspended organic solids are decomposed aerobically by bacteria using oxygen, algae uses carbon dioxide to produce oxygen.

6-3 To remove additional BOD, suspended solids, nutrients and bacterium

6-4 Distribution arm—to spread the wastewater evenly over the media
media—to support the biological growth
underdrains—to collect the flow and transport it out of the filter, provide ventilation, and support the media.

6-5 To remove sloughings from the wastewater prior to discharge.

6-6 A series of plastic disks placed side by side on a shaft. The disks are suspended in a channel of wastewater and rotate through the wastewater.

6-7 Slime on the disk collects organic solids from the wastewater, organisms biologically oxidize the materials to produce stable solids. As the disks move through the air oxygen is transferred to the slime to keep it aerobic. Excess solids are removed as sloughings as the disk moves through the wastewater.

6-8 Biological growth is attached to media

6-9 Units are normally covered and maintain same temperature throughout the year.

6-10 Nitrification is occurring in the later stages of the process.

Chapter 7:

7-1 Mixed liquor

7-2 Activated sludge

7-3 Food, oxygen, organisms

7-4 Provide oxygen and mixing to keep solids in suspension

7-5 Aeration tank color, foam, odors, settling tank clarity, solids loss, aeration rates, process control tests, etc.

7-6 $\dfrac{1200 \text{ mL} \times 1,000}{2,000 \text{ mL}} = 600$

7-7 $\dfrac{415 \times 1,000}{2,350} = 177$

7-8 8,355 mg/L × 0.069 MGD × 8.34 = 4,808

7-9 Contact stabilization

7-10 Conventional sludge process

Chapter 8:

8-1 Disinfection destroys pathogenic organisms. Sterilization destroys all organisms.

8-2 Pathogens

8-3 Demand

8-4 Demand, 1, residual, 30

8-5 Yellow green, 2.5

8-6 Toxic substance

8-7
$$\text{Dose, mg/L} = \frac{387 \text{ lb/day}}{(5.8 \text{ MGD} \times 8.34)} = 8 \text{ mg/L}$$

8-8 7.48

8-9 Chlorine is toxic to receiving water body biota

8-10 $\dfrac{48.3 \text{ lb/day} \times 1.10 \times 365 \text{ days}}{2{,}000 \text{ lb/containers}} = (9.6) \text{ 10 containers}$

Chapter 9:

9-1 Gravity thickeners, flotation thickeners, solids concentrators

9-2 Chemical oxidation, aerobic digestion, anaerobic digestion, lime stabilization, wet air oxidation, incineration

9-3 Sand drying bed, centrifuge, incinerator, filter presses, vacuum filters

9-4 Removes 100% of water, 100% of organic matter and 100% pathogenic organisms

9-5 $\dfrac{325 \text{ mg/L}}{1{,}850 \text{ mg/L}} = 0.18 \text{ lb}$

9-6 Returned to the plant for treatment

9-7 Decrease sludge volume, stabilize organic matter, and recover organic matter for use in the plant.

9-8 Primary organic, solid municipal wastewater product that can be beneficially reused.

9-9 2

9-10 Stabilize organic matter, decrease volume, eliminate pathogenic organisms

Chapter 10:

10-1 15 minutes

10-2 A sample collected all at one time. Representative of the conditions only at the time taken.

10-3 0 milliliters/Liter of copper sulfate—sulfanic acid solution.

10-4 For pH, dissolved oxygen, total residual chlorine, fecal coliform and any test required by NPDES permit for grab sample.

10-5 At different times to allow for the time it takes for wastewater to pass through treatment units.

10-6 A series of samples collected over a specified period of time in proportion to flow.

10-7 Composite samples reflect conditions in wastewater over a period of time.

10-8 Collect from well mixed locations; clearly mark sampling points; easy location to read; no large or unusual particles; no deposits, growths or floating materials; corrosion resistant containers; follow safety procedures; test samples as soon as possible.

10-9 A meter, reference electrode, and glass electrode.

10-10 USEPA Regulation (40 CFR 136) and the plant's permit.

10-11 48 hours when preserved using refrigeration at 4°C.

10-12 day

10-13 In the CBOD test the nitrogenous oxygen demand is eliminated.

10-14 To ensure healthy organisms are available.

10-15 0.6 mg/L – 1.0 mg/L

10-16 Refrigerate at 4°C

10-17 Absorption of water during cooling, contaminants, finger prints, etc.

10-18 Licensed operator/responsible official

Answers to
Comprehensive Review Exam

(1) Prevent disease
Protect aquatic organisms
Protect water quality

(2) Dissolved and suspended

(3) Organic indicates matter that is made up mainly of carbon, hydrogen, and oxygen and will decompose into mainly carbon dioxide and water at 550°C.

(4) Algae, bacteria, protozoa, rotifers, virus

(5) Carbon dioxide, water, more organisms, stable solids

(6) Toxic matter, inorganic dissolved solids, pathogenic organisms

(7) Effluent

(8) From body wastes of humans who have disease

(9) Disease-causing

(10) Domestic waste

(11) Industrial waste

(12) 2.4 ft

(13) 5,250 gal × 8.34 lb/gal = 43,785 lbs

(14) 1,920 ft³ × 7.48 gal/ft³ = 14,362 gal

(15) 30 mg/L × 3.40 MGD × 8.34 lbs/MG/mg/L = 850.7 lbs/day

(16) 25 mg/L × 7.25 MGD × 3.785 KG/MG/mg/L = 686 KG/day

(17) $\dfrac{3{,}280 \text{ lb/day}}{3{,}250 \text{ mg/L} \times 8.34 \text{ lb/MG/mg/L}} = 0.121 \text{ MGD}$

(18) $\dfrac{240 \text{ mg/L} \times 0.72 \text{ MGD} \times 8.34 \text{ lbs/MG/mg/L}}{0.17 \text{ lbs BOD}_5/\text{person/day}} = 8{,}477 \text{ people}$

(19) 8.34 lbs/gal × 1.1288 = 9.41 lbs/gal

223

(20) To remove large objects

(21) Manual and mechanical cleaners

(22) Burial in an approved landfill; incineration

(23) Grit is heavy inorganic matter. Sand, gravel, metal filings, egg shells, coffee grounds, etc.

(24) $\dfrac{8.0 \text{ MGD} \times 1.55 \text{ cfs/MGD}}{3 \text{ channels} \times 2' \times 3'} = 0.7 \text{ fps}$

(25) There is a large amount of organic matter in the grit. The aeration rate must be increased to prevent settling of the organic solids.

(26) To remove settleable and floatable solids.

(27) To remove the settleable solids formed by the biological activity.

(28) $\dfrac{0.785 \times 90' \times 90' \times 12'' \times 7.48 \text{ gal/ft} \times 24 \text{ hrs/day}}{2.25 \text{ MGD} \times 1,000,000 \text{ gal/MG}} = 6.1 \text{ hours}$

$\dfrac{2.25 \text{ MGD} \times 1,000,000 \text{ gal/MG}}{0.785 \times 90' \times 90'} = 354 \text{ gpd/ft}$

$\dfrac{2.25 \text{ MGD} \times 1,000,000 \text{ gal/MG}}{3.14 \times 90'} = 7,962 \text{ gpd/ft}$

(29) Stabilization pond, oxidation pond, polishing pond.

(30) Settling, anaerobic digestion of settled solids, aerobic/anaerobic decomposition of dissolved and colloidal organic solids by bacteria producing stable solids and carbon dioxide, photosynthesis production of oxygen by algae.

(31) Summer effluent is high in solids (algae) and low in BOD_5.
Winter effluent is low in solids and high in BOD_5.

(32) Eliminates wide diurnal and seasonal variation in pond D.O.

(33) Increases during the daylight hours and decreases during darkness.

(34) Reduces fecal coliform, BOD_5, TSS, and nutrient levels.

(35) Distribution system—to distribute the hydraulic and organic loading evenly over the filter media.
Media—to support the biological growth.
Underdrains—to collect and remove treated wastewater and sloughings from the filter. To provide ventilation.

(36) Standard (best effluent quality)
High rate
Roughing

(37) Disks covered with biological growth rotate in wastewater. Organisms collect food during submergence. Oxygen is transferred during exposure to air. Organisms oxidize organic matter. Waste products and sloughings are discharged to wastewater flow for removal in settling tank.

(38) The use of fixed film biological organisms.

(39) Normal—gray, shaggy; High sulfur—chalky, white

(40) Increase waste rate

(41) Decrease; decrease; decrease; increases; increase

(42) 320 lb/hypochlorite × 0.45 available chl. = 144 lb/chl/day

(43)
$$\frac{285 \text{ lb chlorine/day}}{0.679\% \text{ Available Chlorine} \times 8.34 \text{ lb/gal} \times 1.18} = 42.7 \text{ gal/day}$$

(44)
$$\frac{45.8 \text{ lb/day} \times 1.10 \times 365 \text{ days}}{2,000 \text{ lb/containers}} = (9.2) \text{ 10 containers}$$

(45) Disinfection destroys pathogenic organisms
Sterilization destroys all organisms

(46) Demand; 1; residual; 30

(47) Yellow green; 2.5

(48) 30 min/cyc × 24 hrs/3hr/cyc × 70 gpm × 8.34 lb/gal × 0.051 × 0.66 =
4,716 lb/day

(49)
$$\frac{41 \text{ mg} \times 63,000 \text{ gal} \times 3.785 \text{ L/gal}}{1 \text{ L} \times 454 \text{ grams/lb} \times 1,000 \text{ mg/gram}} = 21.5 \text{ lb}$$

(50) The licensed operator and the responsible official.

Commonly Used Formulae in Wastewater Treatment

Parameter	Formula
Area, ft^2	
Rectangle	Width, ft × Length, ft [(W)(L)]
Circle	0.785 (Diameter, ft)^2 [(0.785)D^2]
Volume, ft^3	
Rectangle	Width, ft × Length, ft × Height [(W)(L)(H)]
Cylinder	0.785 (Diameter,ft)^2(Height, ft) [0.785 D^{2}H]
Cone	(1/3)(π)(Radius, ft)^2(Height, ft) [0.33πR^{2}H]
Sphere	(4/3)(π)(Radius,ft)^3 [4.19R^3]
Flow, cfs	(Velocity, ft/sec)(Surface Area, ft^2) [(V)(A)]
Pounds per Day	(Flow, MGD)(con,mg/L)(8.34 lbs/gal) [(Q)(mg/L)(8.34)]
SVI, ml/mg/L	$\dfrac{\text{Volume}}{\text{MLSS concentration}} \times 100$
Circumference, ft	(π)(Diameter)
Detention Time, hrs	$\dfrac{\text{(Volume, gal)(24 hrs/day)}}{\text{Flow, gpd } [V/Q]}$
Surface Loading Rate, gpd/ft^2	$\dfrac{\text{Flow, gpd}}{\text{Area,ft}^2 \ [Q/A]}$
Organic Loading Rate	$\dfrac{\text{lbs of BOD}}{\text{lbs MSVSS}}$
Sludge Age	$\dfrac{\text{MLSS in Aeration Tank}}{\text{SS in Primary Effluent}}$
MCRT	$\dfrac{\text{SS in Secondary System}}{\text{WAS/day + SS in effluent/day}}$
Volatile Solids Reduction	$\dfrac{\text{In} - \text{Out}}{\text{In} - (\text{In} - \text{Out})} \times 100$
Chlorine Dose	Chlorine Demand + Chlorine Residual
Removal, %	In − Out × 100

227

Index

turbulence, 13
titration, 207

vacuum filter, 163–164
velocity, 107
velocity calculation, 62
velocity head, 104, 107
volatile, 13
volatility, 13
volume, 49–58

waste activated sludge solids (WASS), 13
wastewater, 13
wastewater characteristics, 91–105
wastewater solids, 157–170
wastewater sources, 91–108
wastewater testing methods, 176
wastewater treatment ponds, 124–129
weir, 13, 122

Zoogleal slime, 13